Diagnostic Test Package
The Harbrace Handbooks

Prepared by

Bill Spencer
Delta State University

Florida CLAST-Based Diagnostic Tests
Sue Haynes Pine
Florida Community College at Jacksonville

Texas TASP-Based Diagnostic Tests
Laura Ore
Austin Community College

THOMSON
™
HEINLE

Australia   Canada   Mexico   Singapore   Spain   United Kingdom   United States

THOMSON

HEINLE

Hodges' Harbrace Handbook, Fifteenth Edition
The Writer's Harbrace Handbook, Second Edition
Diagnostic Test Package
Bill Spencer, Sue Haynes Pine, Laura Ore

Publisher: *Michael Rosenberg*
Acquisitions Editor: *Dickson Musslewhite*
Development Editor: *Marita Sermolins*
Production Editor: *Lianne Ames*
Marketing Manager: *Katrina Byrd*
Manufacturing Manager: *Marcia Locke*
Compositor: *Nesbitt Graphics*
Cover Designer: *Linda Beaupre*
Printer: *Globus Printing Company*

For more information contact Heinle, 25 Thomson Place, Boston, MA 02210 USA, or you can visit our Internet site at http://www.heinle.com

For permission to use material from this text or product contact us:
Tel   1-800-730-2214
Fax   1-800-730-2215
Web   www.thomsonrights.com

ISBN: 0-8384-0647-5

Contents

GENERAL DIAGNOSTIC TESTS

Description of Tests

This test package contains two basic components: a precourse component and a postcourse component. Each component, in turn, contains both an essay and an objective section. Each objective section is followed by a test answer key and correction chart. The essay sections are accompanied by directions and suggestions for administration, necessary materials, time limits, methods of handling the testing period itself, and the scoring and interpretation of results.

Suggestions for Administration

Necessary materials:

Objective tests: Timer, pens or pencils for students, answer sheets (which may be reproduced from the master answer sheets in this booklet or may be computer cards, Scantron sheets, or notebook paper with answers numbered 1 to 50).

Essay tests: Timer, pens or pencils for students, lined paper or examination ("blue") books.

Time limits: Both objective- and essay-test questions are designed to fit into the standard 50-minute class period, but timing is not essential to test validity. Students may be allotted any amount of time over 50 minutes without compromise of the test's validity.

Administration of the Test

1. To facilitate handling of the completed examinations, both objective and essay, the examiner may wish to provide paper of uniform size.

2. To help reduce the problem of illegible answers, especially to the essay questions, the examiner may insist that students use ink pens, rather than pencils or felt pens. If this regulation is adopted, pens should be supplied by the examiner to prevent off colors of ink, such as magenta and green.

3. Because students may arrive at the examination room without watches, it will be helpful to install a clock visible to everyone in the room or to put the time on a chalkboard at regular intervals during the examination.

4. To reduce required time for the examination, the examiner may wish to instruct the students to cross out and insert freely rather than provide time to recopy answers, especially for essay questions.

5. To reduce students' anxiety, the examiner may wish to explain that these tests will not be used to disqualify students from attendance at the institution and that the scores will be used only to place students in the appropriate levels of composition courses. In any case, the scores will not become part of a student's record unless the examiner wishes to use the scores to exempt a student from a course normally mandated as a graduation requirement. The students can be reassured that they are not expected to know the answers to all the objective questions or to write perfect essays. What they do not know at this stage of their college careers is as important as what they do know.

Scoring and Interpretation of Results

1. The pre- and postcourse tests have approximately the same degree of difficulty, but they have been designed as diagnostic, rather than assessment, instruments. However, if the objective tests are used to determine passing and failing, it will be convenient to use a standard grading scale of

90	to	100%	=	A
80	to	89%	=	B
70	to	79%	=	C
60	to	69%	=	D
00	to	59%	=	F

For each objective test, each question may be counted as two points. Thus, a score of 49 is a 98% mark, etc.

2. The essay tests may be read holistically (on an overall impression basis), especially if they are to be used exclusively for assigning students to the proper levels of courses. If the tests are used to inform the students of their writing weaknesses, the papers can quickly be marked with chapter/section numbers keyed to *The Hodges' Harbrace Handbook*. Such chapter/section references are also convenient as prescriptions for work at a writing laboratory.

3. The tests have been developed for the middle level of freshman composition overall, although individual questions are targeted for less-advanced and more-advanced students. Interpretation of test results should be done with the level of the class and the course curriculum in mind.

How to Read the Answer Keys

The answer key at the end of each objective test provides not only the correct answers but also brief descriptions of the errors and references to the appropriate handbook chapters and sections.

The answer key column that is headed "Section" indicates the relevant sections in *The Hodges' Harbrace Handbook*.

Diagnostic Essay Test, Form A

Directions: Write an essay on *one* of the following topics. Use standard written English and standard format. (For example, use complete sentences, and observe standard five-space paragraph indentation.)

Suggestions: Allow time at the beginning to plan your essay, perhaps by making a brief outline of the main points that you plan to discuss. Allow some time at the end of the examination period to read what you have written and to make editorial and proofreading changes.

Topics

1. Write a detailed article for a hobby magazine describing the benefits and pleasures to be derived from a hobby that you enjoy.

2. Your history teacher has agreed to allow the class to watch a movie if you can convince her that it has historical merit. Write an essay that argues for the movie you want the class to see.

3. Recently, it has come to your attention that you need to budget your time better. In order to help yourself get more organized, write an essay in which you analyze how you waste or misuse time, and give a detailed plan for improving your time management.

4. If you know a seriously handicapped person or someone with a debilitating disease, write an inspirational essay on the contributions of such a person and what he or she has to teach us.

5. If you have ever felt that there was pressure on you not to perform well in school or at a job, write an essay which describes that experience and which helpfully advises others how to deal with such pressure.

6. Nominate a nationally known performer for a "Most Versatile Actor or Actress" award, and support your nomination with details of the performer's varied roles.

7. Argue for the reliability or unreliability of first impressions about other people. Support your position with specific examples from your experience.

8. Write an essay nominating someone you know for the title of "World's Most Annoying Coworker or Boss."

Name_____

Date_____

_____

_____

_____

_____

_____

_____

_____

_____

_____

_____

_____

_____

_____

_____

_____

_____

_____

_____

_____

_____

_____

Diagnostic Objective Test, Form A

Directions: Each of the numbered sentences in this test component has five underlined sections. If one of the underlined sections contains an error in standard written English, mark the letter of that section on your answer sheet. No sentence has more than one error, and some sentences may not contain any errors. If there is no error, mark "E" on your answer sheet.

Sample:

The school <u>principal</u> says <u>that</u> every problem <u>present</u> <u>an</u> opportunity. <u>No error</u>
        A   B   C   D   E

The correct answer is "C." The error is in subject–verb agreement because "problem" is third-person singular and therefore would agree with "presents." In *The Hodges' Harbrace Handbook,* this information is found in section 17e.

1. A student has to be <u>real</u> smart to do <u>well</u> in Prof<u>.</u> Elkins' <u>E</u>nglish class. <u>No error</u>
                          A   B   C   D   E

2. <u>E</u>lvis is not dead<u>,</u> he is just hiding__<u> </u>because he want<u>s</u> some privacy. <u>No error</u>
  A   B   C   D   E

3. <u>After seeing *Star Wars*,</u> I had <u>an</u> argument with my best friend<u>,</u> Dorothy, and was <u>so</u> upset. <u>No error</u>
           A   B   C   C   D   E

4. Although__Luke is <u>an</u> excellent novelist<u>,</u> he is also a poet<u>,</u> and an editor. <u>No error</u>
      A   B   C   D   E

5. After asking us several questions<u>,</u> the manager told my friend and <u>me</u> that <u>we</u> had <u>gotten</u> the job. <u>No error</u>
                         A   B   C   D   E

6. Discussing the <u>serious</u> problems of <u>t</u>eenagers <u>encourage</u> positive <u>psychological</u> results. <u>No error</u>
                A   B   C   D   E

7. Toni Morrison<u>'s</u> novel *Beloved* depicts the lasting__painful effects of slavery on a mother__
            A   B   C
and <u>her</u> children. <u>No error</u>
    D   E

8. All of the <u>childrens</u> <u>mothers</u> requested that school <u>start</u> <u>later</u> in the day. <u>No error</u>
                A   B   C   D   E

9. She <u>would of</u> helped you if <u>only</u> you <u>had</u> <u>asked</u> her nicely. <u>No error</u>
       A   B   C   D   E

10. Manessha<u>'s</u> <u>parents</u> never found out about <u>us</u> going out together <u>every day</u> last month. <u>No error</u>
      A   B   C   D   E

11. Sissy decide<u>d</u> she would rather live in <u>N</u>ew Mexico__so she sold her house__and moved again. <u>No error</u>
           A   B   C   D   E

12. The students should <u>get</u> <u>plenty</u> of sleep so <u>you</u> will be <u>rested</u> for the exam. <u>No error</u>
                  A B   C   D   E

13. <u>Every time</u> she <u>request</u> that song she <u>gets</u> lonely for <u>him</u> all over again. <u>No error</u>
     A   B   C   D   E

14. <u>Due to the fact that</u> taxes <u>have continued</u> to rise, <u>C</u>alifornia voters have revolted__and demanded reform.
         A   B   C   D
<u>No error</u>
 E

15. <u>Singing all the while</u>, the pigs <u>were fed</u> <u>by Jim behind</u> his grandparents' barn each <u>s</u>ummer morning.
         A   B   C   D
<u>No error</u>
 E

16. When the boy returned__from his <u>E</u>nglish class__ he threw down <u>his</u> books. <u>No error</u>
                    A   B   C   D   E

17. Kristi told Amanda <u>that</u> <u>she</u> had <u>been</u> elected president of the local writers<u>'</u> association. <u>No error</u>
                      A B   C   D   E

18. Tara did not just turn in <u>her</u> work<u>,</u> she turn<u>ed</u> in <u>Will's</u> work also. <u>No error</u>
                             A   B   C   D   E

19. <u>Having failed the test</u>, the <u>final</u> grade <u>amazed</u> the <u>student</u>. <u>No error</u>
         A   B   C   D   E

20. The <u>1st</u> law of politics <u>is to get elected;</u> the <u>second</u> law is to stay in office. <u>No error</u>
      A   B   C   D   E

21. We <u>glided</u> <u>easy</u> on the ice once we adjusted <u>our</u> skates <u>properly</u>. <u>No error</u>
        A   B   C   D   E

22. <u>Everyone</u> should do <u>their</u> best to see that <u>A</u>merica remains number one in <u>e</u>ducation. <u>No error</u>
      A   B   C   D   E

23. Even if the spelling bee comes down to a contest <u>between</u> <u>you and I,</u> I will still try <u>my</u> best <u>to win</u>. <u>No error</u>
                                       A   B   C   D   E

24. The students liked <u>professor Ford</u>__because she did not assign homework in her <u>reading</u> or <u>study skills</u> class.
                        A   B   C   D   D
<u>No error</u>
 E

25. The best acting <u>roles</u> in the play were <u>given</u> to Luke and <u>myself</u> because we had the <u>most</u> experience.
                   A   B   C   D
<u>No error</u>
 E

26. The <u>school</u> was <u>hit</u> by a <u>tornado;</u> then the students <u>were</u> sent home. <u>No error</u>
      A   B   C   D   E

27. The <u>student</u>__ was <u>upset</u>__ because <u>his</u> car was <u>busted</u>. <u>No error</u>
               A   B   C   D   E

28. He was the <u>most happiest</u> man in the <u>world</u> <u>because</u> he had a <u>new baby</u> daughter. <u>No error</u>
             A   B   C   D   E

29. <u>Whomever</u> votes in this <u>election</u>__will help change the direction <u>of this planet</u>. <u>No error</u>
    A   B   C   D   E

30. He asked<u>,</u> <u>"Who</u> started the <u>rumor?"</u>. <u>No error</u>
    A   B   C D   E

31. <u>Most</u> anyone can be manipulat<u>ed</u> <u>by such advertising techniques</u> as__<u>subliminal associations</u>. <u>No error</u>
    A   B C   D   E

32. It is a <u>terrible</u> problem<u>,</u> but <u>its</u> <u>their</u> problem. <u>No error</u>
    A   B   C   D   E

33. The train stops in Newark<u>,</u> New Jersey<u>;</u> Atlanta, Georgia<u>;</u> Harrisburg, Pennsylvania<u>;</u> and Valley Stream, Long
    A   B   C   D

    Island. <u>No error</u>
    E

34. She may be happier<u>,</u> smarter<u>,</u> and richer<u>,</u> but she is not better than <u>me</u>. <u>No error</u>
    A   B   C   D   E

35. When it rains <u>all</u> day<u>,</u> I get <u>into</u> a peaceful<u>,</u> happy mood. <u>No error</u>
    A   B   C   D   E

36. Every <u>Summer</u> <u>I</u> exercise at the <u>gym</u>__ and work on <u>my</u> tan. <u>No error</u>
    A   B   C   D   E

37. He had <u>notice</u> the <u>restaurant</u> once before<u>,</u> but he had never actually <u>been</u> there. <u>No error</u>
    A   B   C   D   E

38. To listen to a lecture is difficult; to comprehend it is <u>even more</u> difficult; and <u>remembering</u> it is <u>almost</u>
    A   B   C   D

    impossible. <u>No error</u>
    E

39. I cannot give the restaurant <u>my</u> full endorsement <u>since</u> <u>they</u> do not provide bread with <u>each</u> meal. <u>No error</u>
    A   B   C   D   E

40. Some <u>buildings</u> do not offer access for handicapped persons<u>,</u> and <u>this</u> <u>violates</u> the law. <u>No error</u>
    A   B   C   D   E

Directions: Each of the following passages is followed by a question and five answers. Choose the best answer for each question.

41. The man was bent double like an old hag.

    What figure of speech is used in this sentence?

    A. Simile
    B. Personification
    C. Hyperbole
    D. Metaphor
    E. None of the above

42. 1. A study of one prison showed that owning a pet can change a hardened prison inmate into a more caring person.

2. Another study showed that senior citizens became more interested in life when they were given pets.

3. Even emotionally disturbed children react positively when they hold a soft kitten or puppy.

4. Animals, then, can be a means of therapy for many kinds of individuals.

Which sentence is the topic of this paragraph?

    A.   Sentence 1
    B.   Sentence 2
    C.   Sentence 3
    D.   Sentence 4
    E.   None of the above

43. A vaccine is a preparation of dead or weakened germs, which is injected under the skin and causes the blood to produce antibodies against the disease. Effective vaccines, for instance, have been developed for smallpox, rabies, and polio.

What method of structuring a composition has primarily been used to organize this paragraph?

    A.   Comparison/contrast
    B.   Definition and example
    C.   Enumeration
    D.   Time order
    E.   None of the above

44. The Chinese have an inherent talent for art. Two Chinese girls took an art course with me, and they were the best students in the class.

What logical error is illustrated in this passage?

    A.   Appeal to popularity
    B.   Hasty generalization
    C.   Begging the question
    D.   Irrelevant testimonial
    E.   No error

45. Getting a job can be difficult for a young person. Even if the individual already has some experience with odd jobs, such as babysitting or waiting tables. Especially when the economy is depressed or consumer confidence is low. Which can happen, for example, when the United States' trade deficit increases significantly.

How many fragments are in the above passage?

    A.   One
    B.   Two
    C.   Three
    D.   Four
    E.   None

46. An individual should make plans for the future. When you are planning for the future, you should first decide where you want to be in five years, and obviously a person needs a good education. In fact, I believe that in ten years every job will require a college degree.

What is the writing error in this passage?

   A.   Lack of unity
   B.   Lack of transitions
   C.   Fused sentences
   D.   Unnecessary shift in grammatical person
   E.   None of the above

47. Every weekend athlete is acquainted with the sudden crippling pain known as a "stitch in the side." The stitch is actually a cramp in the diaphragm, the muscle that separates the abdomen from the chest cavity. When you breathe too heavily in a short period of time, the diaphragm suffers an oxygen shortage and reacts with the painful cramp.

What is the writing flaw in this passage?

   A.   Misspelling
   B.   Comma misplacement
   C.   Lack of sentence variety
   D.   Lack of transitions
   E.   No error

48. What is the writing flaw in the following sentence?

Some critics believe that the creators of the space program not only seek scientific understanding, but also they are seeking publicity.

   A.   Clichés
   B.   Lack of parallelism
   C.   Euphemisms
   D.   Dense noun phrases
   E.   None of the above

49. It was Christmas. I was four. Tommy was eight. We received a baseball and a bat. Our faces lit up with joy. We wanted a place to play. Tommy began to think of a place.

What is the most serious writing problem with the above passage?

   A.   Clichés
   B.   Sentence fragments
   C.   Choppiness
   D.   Passive voice
   E.   None of the above

50. Carlieze loves flowers. Such as roses, daisies, and African violets. She collects them. Whenever she gets the chance. Which, unfortunately, is not very often.

How many fragments are there in the above passage?

   A.   One
   B.   Two
   C.   Three
   D.   Four
   E.   None

Diagnostic Objective Test, Form A

Answer Sheet

Name_____

Date_____

1. _____   20. _____   39. _____

2. _____   21. _____   40. _____

3. _____   22. _____   41. _____

4. _____   23. _____   42. _____

5. _____   24. _____   43. _____

6. _____   25. _____   44. _____

7. _____   26. _____   45. _____

8. _____   27. _____   46. _____

9. _____   28. _____   47. _____

10. _____   29. _____   48. _____

11. _____   30. _____   49. _____

12. _____   31. _____   50. _____

13. _____   32. _____   Score _____

14. _____   33. _____

15. _____   34. _____

16. _____   35. _____

17. _____   36. _____

18. _____   37. _____

19. _____   38. _____

Diagnostic Objective Test Answer Key, Form A

Question	Answer	*Hodges'* Section	*Writer's* Section
1	A	4b	20b
2	B	3a	19a
3	D	22c	23h
4	D	13	31g
5	E	5b	21b
6	C	6a	22e
7	B	12c	31c
8	A	15a	33a
9	A	7a	22a
10	C	5c	21c
11	C	12a	31a
12	C	27b	N/A
13	B	6a	22e
14	A	21b	30b
15	A	25a	20e
16	C	12b	31b
17	B	28a	21e
18	B	3a	19a
19	A	25a	20e
20	A	11f	39f
21	B	4b	20b
22	B	6b	21d
23	B	5b	21b
24	A	9b	37b
25	C	5b	21b
26	E	14a	32a
27	D	19c	28c
28	A	4c	20c
29	A	5c	21c
30	D	17b	35b
31	A	19c	28c
32	C	15b	33b
33	E	14b	32b
34	D	5c	21c
35	E	12	31
36	A	9e	37e
37	A	7a	22a
38	C	26a	25a
39	C	28c	21e
40	C	28c	21e
41	A	20a	29a
42	D	31a	3c
43	B	31c	2d
44	B	35f	7i
45	C	2	18
46	D	27b	N/A
47	E	31b	3c
48	B	26d	25d
49	C	30a	27a
50	C	2	18

Essay Posttest, Form A

Directions: Write an essay on *one* of the following topics. Use standard written English and standard format. (For example, use complete sentences, and observe standard five-space paragraph indentation.)

Suggestions: Allow time at the beginning to plan your essay, perhaps by making a brief outline of the main points that you plan to discuss. Allow some time at the end of the examination period to read what you have written and to make editorial and proofreading changes.

Topics

1. Drawing on your own experiences, write an essay that supports the assertion that travel is educational.

2. Every year your favorite sports magazine chooses a Sports Person of the Year based on nominations from its readers. Write an essay that nominates the person you would like to see chosen this year, and support your nomination with convincing specifics.

3. Write a letter to the editor of either your school newspaper or your school yearbook suggesting specific ways in which you believe it could be improved.

4. Nominate one of your former teachers for an "Outstanding Teacher Award." Support your argument with details about your nominee's performance as a teacher and counselor.

5. Analyze the various ways in which driving a motorized vehicle (such as a car, truck, or motorcycle) can change a person's language and behavior. Try also to explain the reasons for these changes.

6. Write an essay praising a TV series for helping to weaken some stereotype because it presents a particular group, gender, or race in a complex, balanced manner. Support your praise with specific examples.

7. Analyze the principal causes behind student alcohol abuse, and recommend actions that the schools and local governments could take to alleviate the problem.

8. Write a well-supported essay in which you nominate someone you know for the title "The World's Most Annoying Relative."

Essay Posttest, Form A

Name_____

Date_____

_____

_____

_____

_____

_____

_____

_____

_____

_____

_____

_____

_____

_____

_____

_____

_____

_____

_____

_____

_____

_____

_____

Objective Posttest, Form A

Directions: Each of the numbered sentences in this test component has five underlined sections. If one of the underlined sections contains an error in standard written English, mark the letter of that section. No sentence has more than one error, and some sentences may not contain any errors. If there is no error, mark "E" on your answer sheet.

Sample:

The school <u>principal</u> says <u>that</u> every problem <u>present an</u> opportunity. <u>No error</u>
       A   B   C   D   E

The correct answer is "C." The error is in subject–verb agreement because "problem" is third-person singular and therefore would agree with "presents." In *The Hodges' Harbrace Handbook,* this information is found in section 17e.

1. Farzad<u>'s</u> ances<u>tors</u> owned thousands of acre<u>'s</u> of land in Iran before the revolution <u>there</u>. <u>No error</u>
      A   B   C   D   E

2. I tried repeatedly to contact Mr<u>.</u> McCarthy<u>,</u> however<u>,</u> he refused <u>to</u> write back. <u>No error</u>
                              A   B   C   D   E

3. After <u>examining</u> me, the doctors <u>come</u> to the conclusion that <u>I</u> <u>had</u> Crohn's disease. <u>No error</u>
         A   B   C D   E

4. <u>Me</u> and two of my neighbors watch soap operas__and situation comedies on television <u>almost</u> <u>every day</u>.
   A   B   C   D
<u>No error</u>
  E

5. Mr. King<u>,</u> who is my speech teacher<u>,</u> plays the guitar__and writes unusual<u>,</u> grotesque poetry. <u>No error</u>
        A   B   C   D   E

6. If everyone would concentrate on <u>their</u> own flaws<u>,</u> the world probably <u>would be</u> safer__and happier. <u>No error</u>
                              A   B   C   D   E

7. Although__Carolyn does like to travel in Ireland during the <u>summer months.</u> She is <u>too</u> busy to go this year.
         A   B   C   D
<u>No error</u>
  E

8. Patti wondered <u>whether</u> Tim would ask <u>her</u> to the dance__ or whether she would have to ask <u>him?</u> <u>No error</u>
                 A   B   C   D   E

9. Don't <u>never</u> annoy <u>an</u> alligator<u>,</u> a poisonous snake, or a sleep<u>-</u>deprived raccoon. <u>No error</u>
          A   B   C   D   E

10. Once you have <u>eaten</u> a huge <u>Thanksgiving</u> dinner<u>,</u> it is time to <u>lay</u> down for a nap. <u>No error</u>
                A   B   C   D   E

11. Only <u>one</u> out of <u>every</u> <u>8</u> persons who reach retirement age can expect to be financial<u>ly</u> secure. <u>No error</u>
       A   B C   D   E

12. After the spring wedding <u>ceremony</u> the florist, the caterer, and the musicians__<u>divided</u> the money <u>between</u>
                       A   B   C   D

    them. <u>No error</u>
               E

13. There <u>was</u> fire<u>,</u> flames, and smoke everywhere <u>that</u> they <u>could</u> see. <u>No error</u>
           A   B   C   D   E

14. Laura was a cheerleader__ and had just <u>received</u> her driver<u>'s</u> <u>license</u>. <u>No error</u>
                             A   B   C D   E

15. My <u>Biology</u> professor, Dr. Darwin, is a renowned naturalist<u>,</u> but his true passion is <u>astronomy</u>. <u>No error</u>
        A   B   C   D   E

16. Tolstoy wrote that__ all happy families are alike<u>;</u> whereas each unhappy family <u>is</u> unhappy in <u>its</u> own way.
                        A   B   C   D

    <u>No error</u>
          E

17. He was <u>advised</u> that he needed to work <u>as fast</u>, or faster than<u>,</u> the other employees if <u>he</u> wanted to keep his job.
              A   B   C   D

    <u>No error</u>
          E

18. My conversations with Matthew <u>usually</u> consisted of <u>him</u> telling me jokes__ and reminding me about following
                                              A   B   C

    the doctor<u>'s</u> orders. <u>No error</u>
              D   E

19. If a child misbehaved<u>,</u> his or her name would go on the board and <u>they</u> would not <u>receive</u> a treat at the <u>day's</u>
                         A   B   C   D

    end. <u>No error</u>
            E

20. Neither the Falcons__ nor <u>their</u> coach <u>have</u> predicted <u>a</u> winning season. <u>No error</u>
                       A   B   C   D   E

21. <u>Who</u> will you vote for <u>if</u> the election <u>becomes</u> a three-way <u>contest?</u> <u>No error</u>
        A   B   C   D E

22. According to the <u>principal</u>, the school calendar called <u>for</u> a <u>shorten</u> day the <u>last</u> day of the year. <u>No error</u>
                     A   B   C   D   E

23. Sometimes one has <u>to</u> put <u>their</u> foot down to keep <u>from</u> being <u>abused</u> any longer. <u>No error</u>
                        A   B   C   D   E

24. He <u>prefers</u> his pizza smothered <u>in</u> cheese, heaped with pepperoni<u>,</u> and <u>an extra sprinkle of black olives doesn't</u>
         A   B   C   D

    <u>hurt</u> <u>No error</u>
             E

25. When my mother was in the hospital<u>,</u> my father <u>asked</u> my brothers__and <u>me</u> to look after her. <u>No error</u>
                                A   B   C   D   E

26. The cheese was melted all over the beef, which smelled different than usual, later I would find out why.
                                                   A   B   C   D
   No error
     E

27. Although he did enjoy Florida, he kept thinking that he could have went to Cancun instead. No error
                  A   B   C   D   E

28. There are many films based on Twain's classic novel "Adventures of Huckleberry Finn." No error
   A B   C   D   D   E

29. Set in the Mississippi Delta__ the novel__Wolf Whistle__ has so far received the most awards of any Lewis
                              A   B   B   C   D
   Nordan novel. No error
             E

30. To err is human; to forgive is divine; but forgetting is nearly impossible. No error
     A   B   C   D   E

31. The use of muted trumpets__and saxophones give the song an exciting, jazzy sound. No error
                          A   B   C   D   E

32. Though it is too crowded sometimes, Guadalajara is a fairly good restaurant when there is a reasonable amount
                   A   B   C   D
   of people there. No error
              E

33. In addition to the meals on the menu, items that you choose from includes a soup, fruit, and salad bar.
   A   B   C   D
   No error
     E

34. If you stopped smoking, you can reverse some of the damage done to your heart and lungs. No error
      A   B   C   D   E

35. Rick does not hardly know how to carry on a conversation for more than a minute. No error
              A   B   C   D   E

36. Have you ever had an old relative who is an annoying pest or even a menace to society. No error
                  A   B   C   D E

37. When she passed the age of seventy, she would sing alot whenever she got intoxicated. No error
          A   B   C   D   E

38. Miss Florida was more beautiful than any contestant in the Miss America pageant. No error
               A   B   C   D   E

39. A symbol is when an object richly suggests several meanings at the same time. No error
          A B   C   D   E

40. The poem "Dover Beach" by Matthew Arnold__ expresses the poet's need for security in a chaotic world.
          A   A   B   C   D
   No error
     E

Directions: Each of the passages below is followed by some questions. Choose the best answer for each question.

In Florida, there are beautiful beaches on all the coasts. There are also several enjoyable theme parks in central Florida, as well as a number of interesting natural attractions. Furthermore, there is the excitement of big, cosmopolitan cities and the charm of quaint, historic villages.

41. The passage lacks

    A.   logic.
    B.   transitions.
    C.   adjectives.
    D.   a topic sentence.
    E.   none of the above.

42. The passage achieves coherence through

    A.   repeated words/synonyms.
    B.   parallel structures.
    C.   transition words.
    D.   all of the above.
    E.   none of the above.

A reliable calendar helped religious groups, such as the Christians, fix the dates of important holy days like Christmas and Easter. Furthermore, seasonal variables such as rainfall and temperature could now be predicted, enabling farmers to plant at the best time. Most important, the accurate measurement of time would become perhaps the one aspect of life on which nearly all civilized nations could agree.

43. Which of the following would be the best topic sentence for this passage?

    A.   Discovering accurate ways to measure and divide time influenced civilization in a number of ways.
    B.   The solar and lunar calendars differed in accuracy.
    C.   Modern societies owe their very existence to the discovery of accurate ways of measuring time.
    D.   Any of the above.
    E.   None of the above.

44. In what kind of order are the supporting statements in this passage presented?

    A.   Order of importance
    B.   Chronological order
    C.   Spatial order
    D.   General to specific
    E.   None of the above

45. Which of the following would be an appropriate concluding statement for the passage?

    A.   If calendars had never been invented, mankind would still be living in caves.
    B.   Therefore, you should be grateful to those who invented clocks and calendars; without them, your life would be impossible.
    C.   So it is with all great discoveries: after a while society inevitably begins to take them for granted.
    D.   Of course, Columbus' discovery of the new world was highly significant also, but that's another story.
    E.   None of the above.

Directions: Choose the best option.

46. Given the topic sentence "New York City is a great place to spend a vacation," which of the supporting statements below would be irrelevant?

A. A visitor could spend weeks in museums such as the Guggenheim, the Museum of Natural History, and the Cloisters.
B. Sights such as the World Trade Center and the New York Stock Exchange are fascinating and educational.
C. Violent crimes, especially rape and muggings, are on the increase in all parts of the city.
D. Entertainment possibilities range from Shakespeare to baseball.
E. None of the above.

47. "The incompetence and greed of petty politicians have all but destroyed our city! Nothing works anymore—not the garbage collection, not the police force, and especially not the mayor's office."

The tone of this passage may best be described as

A. objective.
B. humorous.
C. angry.
D. optimistic.
E. none of the above.

48. Cindy tried to withdraw from the race, and she was elected president anyway.

What is the writing flaw in this sentence?

A. Incorrect punctuation
B. Comma splice
C. Tense shift
D. Faulty coordination
E. None of the above

49. Which of the following sentences qualifies as a thesis statement for a persuasive essay?

A. The legal drinking age is twenty-one.
B. Drinking is not permitted on campus.
C. Students should be allowed to have beer on campus.
D. Some bottles of beer cost less than a dollar.
E. None of the above.

50. Carolyn writes poetry, and she teaches science fiction, and she edits booklets, and she conducts workshops.

What is the writing flaw in the above sentence?

A. Stringy, compound structure
B. Unnecessary commas
C. Fused sentences
D. Lack of parallelism
E. None of the above

Objective Posttest, Form A

Name_____

Answer Sheet

Date_____

1. _____   20. _____   39. _____

2. _____   21. _____   40. _____

3. _____   22. _____   41. _____

4. _____   23. _____   42. _____

5. _____   24. _____   43. _____

6. _____   25. _____   44. _____

7. _____   26. _____   45. _____

8. _____   27. _____   46. _____

9. _____   28. _____   47. _____

10. _____   29. _____   48. _____

11. _____   30. _____   49. _____

12. _____   31. _____   50. _____

13. _____   32. _____   Score _____

14. _____   33. _____

15. _____   34. _____

16. _____   35. _____

17. _____   36. _____

18. _____   37. _____

19. _____   38. _____

Diagnostic Objective Posttest Answer Key, Form A

<u>Question</u>	<u>Answer</u>	<u>*Hodges'* Section</u>	<u>*Writer's* Section</u>
1	C	15a	33a
2	B	3a	19a
3	B	7a	22a
4	A	5b	21b
5	E	12	31
6	A	6b	21d
7	C	2	18
8	D	17b	35b
9	A	4e	20g
10	D	7a	22a
11	C	11f	39f
12	D	19c	28c
13	A	6a	22e
14	E	13a	31g
15	A	9e	37e
16	B	14c	32c
17	B	22c	23g
18	B	5c	21c
19	B	6b	21d
20	C	6a	22e
21	A	5c	21c
22	C	18b	36b
23	B	6b	21d
24	D	26a	25a
25	E	5b	21b
26	C	3a	19a
27	D	7a	22a
28	C	16b	34b
29	A	12b	31b
30	C	26a	25a
31	B	6a	22e
32	D	19c	28c
33	D	6a	22e
34	C	7d	22d
35	A	4e	20g
36	D	17b	35b
37	C	18	36
38	C	22c	23h
39	A	23d	23d
40	E	16b	34b
41	D	31a	3c
42	D	31b	3c
43	A	31a	3c
44	A	31c	2d
45	E	31a	3c
46	C	31a	3c
47	C	19a	28a
48	D	24b	24b
49	C	32c	2b
50	A	24b	24b

Diagnostic Essay Test, Form B

Directions: Write an essay on *one* of the following topics. Use standard written English and standard format. (For example, use complete sentences, and observe standard five-space paragraph indentation.)

Suggestions: Allow time at the beginning to plan your essay, perhaps by making a brief outline of the main points that you plan to discuss. Allow some time at the end of the examination period to read what you have written and to make editorial and proofreading changes.

Topics

1. Write a helpful, reassuring essay that advises others how to cope with embarrassing moments by showing how you yourself have learned to cope with them.

2. By drawing on your own and friends' experience, warn people about the temptations and consequences of spending money in foolish ways.

3. Often a good education has the effect of teaching us that we don't know as much about an issue or an idea as we thought we knew. Show how a particular experience you've had—in or out of class—has taught you to question and qualify what, before, you thought you had already figured out.

4. Write an essay that gives advice to parents about whether they should encourage, tolerate, or discourage their children's competition with each other. Support your argument with specific, actual examples.

5. In order to warn or advise your audience, narrate the details of an experience in which you gave in to others' pressures and later regretted it.

6. Nominate a small town to be included in a book entitled *The 100 Most Interesting Small Towns in America,* and support your nomination with plenty of relevant details.

7. If you find a particular TV commercial offensive, write an essay aimed at the promoting company, persuading its executives to discontinue the commercial.

8. The Academy of Motion Picture Arts and Sciences is asking for help in selecting one movie produced in the 20th century that best illustrates, for good or ill, the values and ideas for which 20th-century America will be most remembered. Write a carefully organized essay that nominates the movie you believe should be selected.

Name_____

Date_____

_____

_____

_____

_____

_____

_____

_____

_____

_____

_____

_____

_____

_____

_____

_____

_____

_____

_____

_____

_____

_____

_____

Diagnostic Objective Test, Form B

Directions: Each of the numbered sentences in this test component has five underlined sections. If one of the underlined sections contains an error in standard written English, mark the letter of that section on your answer sheet. No sentence has more than one error, and some sentences may not contain any errors. If there is no error, mark "E" on your answer sheet.

Sample:

Some believe the Shroud of <u>T</u>urin is a <u>R</u>enaissance painting<u>,</u> others believe <u>it</u> is the burial cloth of Christ. <u>No error</u>
               A   B   C   D   E

The correct answer is "C." The error is a comma splice because a comma is inadequate punctuation between two complete sentences. In *The Hodges' Harbrace Handbook,* this information is found in section 14a.

1. The Internet offers <u>so</u> much information__that it should appeal to <u>most</u> anyone interested in <u>e</u>ducation.
                   A   B   C   D
<u>No error</u>
  E

2. Though Cormac McCarthy <u>won</u> the National Book Award for his sixth novel<u>,</u> *All the Pretty Horses*<u>,</u> his
                        A   B   C
masterpiece is actually__*Suttree.* <u>No error</u>
                D   E

3. Maria<u>'s</u> grandmother thought about her childhood for <u>a while</u>, and then she <u>begin</u> <u>to get</u> angry. <u>No error</u>
    A   B   C   D   E

4. The side <u>e</u>ffects of this therapy <u>lasts</u> four <u>to</u> five days<u>,</u> and the recovery rate is high. <u>No error</u>
       A   B   C   D   E

5. Nora's husband treat<u>ed</u> her like a <u>child. This</u> eventually <u>caused</u> serious marital problems. <u>No error</u>
                   A   B   C   D   E

6. A <u>G</u>reek tragedy <u>is when</u> <u>there</u> is a catastrophic ending <u>to</u> the play and a catharsis. <u>No error</u>
   A   B   C   D   E

7. Freud theorized that everyone <u>has</u> self-destructive <u>tendencies,</u> <u>but some</u> healthy individuals seem to overcome
                                 A   B C
<u>this</u>. <u>No error</u>
  D   E

8. <u>In this day and age in which we live</u>, it is more important <u>than</u> ever before__to stay informed about the <u>effects</u>
                A   B   C   D
of technological advances. <u>No error</u>
                        E

9. The impact must <u>of</u> <u>rattled</u> the circuits in the <u>television because</u> the screen went blank__and never worked
                   A B   C   D
again. <u>No error</u>
      E

10. <u>Sitting in the back seat,</u> the car trip to <u>North Carolina</u> was not as boring <u>for</u> my brother and <u>me</u> as we had
    feared.
          A   B   C   D
    <u>No error</u>
      E

11. <u>There</u> <u>is</u> a <u>bucket,</u> a hose, and <u>a lot</u> of rags in the garage. <u>No error</u>
  A B   C   D   E

12. The member of the Chicago <u>Bulls, who has scored the most points,</u> will receive a <u>raise</u> <u>beginning</u> January 1,
                                  A   B   C   D
    1998. <u>No error</u>
       E

13. For many years the <u>government</u> has kept track of the <u>amount</u> of people__who <u>are</u> employed. <u>No error</u>
                      A   B   C   D   E

14. <u>Seated behind the wheel</u> of the car__the boy <u>began</u> to drive__to his house. <u>No error</u>
        A   B   C   D   E

15. When <u>your</u> going to create a new product, you must <u>use</u> your <u>imagination.</u> <u>No error</u>
       A   B   C   D   E

16. <u>Speaking from personal experience,</u> the lecture material was <u>unrelated to</u> the <u>course</u> <u>objectives.</u> <u>No error</u>
            A   B   C   D   E

17. After__he <u>left</u> the classroom, the boy thought he had <u>pass</u> the test. <u>No error</u>
   A   B   C   D   E

18. One contestant <u>said</u> she worried the most <u>about the health</u> of her <u>family,</u> another said she worried most about
            A   B   C
    her <u>complexion.</u> <u>No error</u>
      D   E

19. <u>People who teach students</u> can <u>expect</u> many emotional <u>and</u> spiritual <u>rewards</u> but few financial ones. <u>No error</u>
         A   B   C   D   E

20. The Boy Scouts collected old magazines__and newspapers at Christmas, and <u>were</u> able to <u>raise</u> a lot of money.
                                     A   B   C   D
    <u>No error</u>
      E

21. Bill<u>'s</u> mother offered my sister and <u>I</u> a ride to the <u>college</u> campus. <u>No error</u>
  A B   C   D   E

22. Bruce didn't feel <u>like</u> he <u>belonged</u> in <u>this</u> <u>type</u> of work. <u>No error</u>
               A   B   C D   E

23. This <u>summer</u> a group of students will go rafting on the <u>Chatooga</u> <u>river</u> for <u>college</u> credit. <u>No error</u>
      A   B   C   D   E

24. She thought she <u>had done</u> <u>real</u> <u>well</u> on the physics test yesterday. <u>No error</u>
              A   B   C   D   E

25. To pay <u>for</u> <u>your</u> garbage collection, you may be required to <u>mail</u> a check to the city's water <u>dept.</u> <u>No error</u>
       A B   C   D   E

26. When I found the <u>old, rotting</u> directions to the <u>forbidden</u> mine, it became <u>more clearer</u> to me. <u>No error</u>
                  A   B   C   D   E

27. <u>"</u>Who started the rumor<u>?"</u>, he <u>asked</u>. <u>No error</u>
  A   B C   D   E

28. Tess predicts that <u>she</u> <u>could</u> win the <u>beauty</u> pageant if she becomes a <u>blonde</u>. <u>No error</u>
                   A   B   C   D   E

29. All of my students <u>were</u> <u>quite</u> <u>effected</u> by the poetry reading last night. <u>No error</u>
                       A   B   C   D   E

30. When <u>d</u>ad got home, my <u>m</u>other whispered directions to my <u>b</u>rother and <u>me</u> about the party. <u>No error</u>
        A   B   C   D   E

31. Marlana taught me <u>how</u> to cook <u>with</u> unusual <u>spices,</u> such <u>as:</u> coriander, cumin, and curry. <u>No error</u>
                      A   B   C   D   E

32. Because they are cautious, the Elkins twins are <u>only going</u> to explore the <u>first two</u> rooms of the <u>cavern</u>. <u>No error</u>
                     A   B   C   D   E

33. <u>Neither</u> the attorney nor the judges <u>was</u> going <u>to attend</u> the trial. <u>No error</u>
    A   B   C   D   E

34. I went to <u>Gatlinburg,</u> and I brought home <u>3</u> souvenirs for my <u>mother</u>. <u>No error</u>
              A   B   C   D   E

35. Rain <u>is</u> <u>as scarce</u> in <u>Texas</u> as Florida. <u>No error</u>
     A B   C   D   E

36. After we found a <u>good</u> place to <u>sit</u> on the beach, we sunbathed for <u>awhile</u>. <u>No error</u>
                 A   B   C   D   E

37. <u>Let's</u> <u>go</u> to Toledo next summer and visit my <u>Aunt</u>. <u>No error</u>
    A B   C   D   E

38. <u>"</u>Jenny<u>",</u> he said, <u>"</u>let's have <u>lunch."</u> <u>No error</u>
  A   B   C   D E

39. If I <u>was</u> you, I would not <u>go</u> to the <u>movie</u> with Harry. <u>No error</u>
      A   B   C   D   E

40. <u>K</u>elly discovered that it was <u>me</u> <u>who</u> called. <u>No error</u>
   A   B   C D   E

Directions: Each of the passages below is followed by a question and five answers. Choose the best answer for each question.

41. The man said, "I will love you until all the rivers run dry."

What figure of speech is used in the above sentence?

A. Simile
B. Personification
C. Hyperbole/overstatement
D. Metaphor
E. None of the above

42. 1. Sunbathing can be dangerous to your health.
    2. Overexposure to the sun is the prime cause of skin cancer.
    3. Studies indicate that sunbathing is responsible for premature aging and wrinkles.
    4. In addition, overexposure to the sun can cause a painful sunburn.

    Which sentence is the topic sentence of this paragraph?

    A. Sentence 1
    B. Sentence 2
    C. Sentence 3
    D. Sentence 4
    E. None of the above

43. There are significant differences between suburban residents and people in cities. Those who move to the suburbs tend to be younger, to have more children, and to have a higher level of educational accomplishments. Suburbanites also tend to be more affluent than those who remain in the city. Thus the consumer-behavior patterns of suburban and urban consumers also differ greatly.

    What method of structuring a composition has the writer relied on most heavily to organize this paragraph?

    A. Comparison/contrast
    B. Definition
    C. Narration
    D. Time order
    E. None of the above

44. I was like "No way!" And then she goes, "I'm not lying," but then I was like "Oh yeah, I'm sure I believe *that*."

    What is the writing flaw in the preceding passage?

    A. Lack of transitions
    B. Colloquial or informal language
    C. Misuse of quotation marks
    D. Misused exclamation point
    E. None of the above

45. As sure as you're born, air pollution is going to be a tough nut to crack. It is harmful and ugly as sin. Soon there may be a mass exodus from big cities as people begin to avoid them like the plague. To make a long story short, we will have to fight air pollution to the bitter end.

    What is the writing flaw in the above passage?

    A. Dangling modifiers
    B. Clichés
    C. Misspellings
    D. Fused sentences
    E. None of the above

46. The UFO sightings in New Hampshire left many people so startled and more bewildered.

    What is the writing error in this passage?

    A. Capitalization
    B. Misspellings
    C. Incomplete comparisons
    D. Punctuation
    E. None of the above

47. In the movie *The Shining*, Jack Nicholson gives a vivid performance as a man sinking into madness. He suffers at first from mild hallucinations. Then he has a drink in an imaginary bar. Finally, he chases his wife through a deserted hotel.

What is the writing flaw in this passage?

    A.   Misspelling
    B.   Comma misplacement
    C.   Excessive subordination
    D.   Absence of transitions
    E.   None of the above

48. Which one of the following sentences qualifies as a workable thesis for a persuasive essay?

    A.   Some schools print their own newspapers.
    B.   Journalism classes may be given responsibility for a school newspaper.
    C.   A high school newspaper should be protected from administrative censorship.
    D.   News censorship involves restrictions on what kinds of stories and articles may be printed.
    E.   None of the above.

49. Identify the illogical statement(s).

    A.   Former President Clinton's proposed health plan was a bad idea because he is an adulterer.
    B.   A sharp increase in the number of school shootings coincided with the increasing popularity of computer games, so clearly the games are causing the increased violence.
    C.   Since all humans need air to live, air is one of our survival requirements.
    D.   A and B.
    E.   None of the above.

50. It isn't always smooth sailing on the road of life.

What is the writing flaw in this sentence?

    A.   Mixed metaphor
    B.   Misspellings
    C.   Shift from direct to indirect discourse
    D.   Unnecessary shift in voice
    E.   None of the above

Diagnostic Objective Test, Form B

Name_____

Answer Sheet

Date_____

1. _____   20. _____   39. _____

2. _____   21. _____   40. _____

3. _____   22. _____   41. _____

4. _____   23. _____   42. _____

5. _____   24. _____   43. _____

6. _____   25. _____   44. _____

7. _____   26. _____   45. _____

8. _____   27. _____   46. _____

9. _____   28. _____   47. _____

10. _____   29. _____   48. _____

11. _____   30. _____   49. _____

12. _____   31. _____   50. _____

13. _____   32. _____   Score _____

14. _____   33. _____

15. _____   34. _____

16. _____   35. _____

17. _____   36. _____

18. _____   37. _____

19. _____   38. _____

Diagnostic Objective Test Answer Key, Form B

<u>Question</u>	<u>Answer</u>	<u>*Hodges'* Section</u>	<u>*Writer's* Section</u>
1	C	19c	28c
2	D	10a	38a
3	C	7a	22a
4	B	6a	22e
5	C	28c	21e
6	B	23d	23d
7	D	28c	21e
8	A	21b	30b
9	A	7a	22a
10	A	25a	20e
11	B	6a	22e
12	A	13d	31g
13	B	19c	28c
14	B	12b	31b
15	A	18c	36c
16	A	25b	20f
17	D	7a	22a
18	C	3a	19a
19	A	21b	30b
20	B	13a	31g
21	C	5b	21b
22	A	19c	28c
23	C	9a	37a
24	B	4b	20b
25	D	11d	39d
26	D	4c	20c
27	C	13d	37g
28	B	27a	N/A
29	C	19c	28c
30	A	9a	37a
31	D	17d	35d
32	B	25a	20e
33	C	6a	22e
34	C	11f	39f
35	D	26b	25b
36	D	19c	28c
37	D	9e	37e
38	B	16d	34d
39	A	7d	22d
40	C	5b	21b
41	C	20a	29a
42	A	31a	3c
43	A	31c	2d
44	B	19c	28c
45	B	20b	29b
46	C	22c	23g
47	E	31b	3c
48	C	32c	2b
49	D	35f	7i
50	A	20a	29a

Essay Posttest, Form B

Directions: Write an essay on *one* of the following topics. Use standard written English and standard format. (For example, use complete sentences, and observe standard five-space paragraph indentation.)

Suggestions: Allow time at the beginning to plan your essay, perhaps by making a brief outline of the main points that you plan to discuss. Allow some time at the end of the examination period to read what you have written and to make editorial and proofreading changes.

Topics

1. Part of becoming more mature is learning that people do not have to look (or act or talk, etc.) as we think people *should* look (or act or talk, etc.) to be wonderful people whose friendships can teach us a lot. Write an essay which illustrates this point, using at least two specific examples of unusual friends you have had (perhaps from a different culture or age group or economic background).

2. If your family has a unique or little-known tradition for celebrating a certain day, event, or circumstance, describe it and analyze its importance to your family.

3. Analyze the reasons, both obvious and subtle, for the tremendous popularity of soap operas.

4. Write an essay that shows how the knowledge you've acquired in two different courses has worked together to teach you something that neither course could have by itself.

5. Your student government organization is considering instituting a new award for an outstanding student. In a carefully organized and developed essay, discuss the need for such an award, the criteria on which it should be based, and the selection process involved.

6. Recommend the most interesting work of literature that you read last year by discussing in detail what made this piece of literature so memorable or so powerful. Avoid merely summarizing the plot.

7. Nominate a movie that you think deserves to be considered one of the ten best films ever made. Support your nomination with persuasive points and plenty of relevant details.

8. Write a review recommending what you think is the most interesting good restaurant in the area (150-mile radius). Be sure to include the details that make it sound like a fascinating, colorful place.

Essay Posttest, Form B

Name_____

Answer Sheet

Date_____

_____

_____

_____

_____

_____

_____

_____

_____

_____

_____

_____

_____

_____

_____

_____

_____

_____

_____

_____

_____

_____

_____

Objective Posttest, Form B

Directions: Each of the numbered sentences in this test component has five underlined sections. If one of the underlined sections contains an error in standard written English, mark the letter of that section on your answer sheet. No sentence has more than one error, and some sentences may not contain any errors. If there is no error, mark "E" on your answer sheet.

Sample:

Some believe the Shroud of <u>T</u>urin is a <u>R</u>enaissance painting<u>,</u> others believe <u>it</u> is the burial cloth of Christ. <u>No error</u>
              A   B   C   D   E

The correct answer is "C." The error is a comma splice because a comma is inadequate punctuation between two complete sentences. In *The Hodges' Harbrace Handbook,* this information is found in section 14a.

1. Maya Angelou speaks proud<u>ly</u> and lustily in her poem <u>"</u>Phenomenal Woman," and <u>this</u> makes the poem
                            A   B   C D
   more vivid. <u>No error</u>
              E

2. The pumpkins that Bill <u>grows</u> <u>are</u> <u>really</u> large <u>in size</u>. <u>No error</u>
                     A   B   C   D   E

3. <u>You</u> don't see records for <u>sale</u> anymore<u>,</u> only cassettes and <u>compact discs</u>. <u>No error</u>
   A   B   C   D   E

4. Other interests that Kevin <u>has</u> <u>is</u> <u>camping,</u> <u>reading</u>, and music. <u>No error</u>
                          A B   C   D   E

5. When John and <u>me</u> got to the kitchen<u>,</u> we saw <u>two</u> tennis rackets <u>in the corner</u>. <u>No error</u>
                   A   B   C   D   E

6. Recently, Marilyn and Scott<u>__</u> spent their vacation<u>__</u> visiting <u>i</u>ndian ruins in <u>A</u>rizona. <u>No error</u>
                       A   B   C   D   E

7. As he told the ghost story<u>,</u> the fire sizzled<u>,</u> popped, and showered sparks<u>,</u> making us even more frighten<u>ed</u>.
                   A   B   C   D
  <u>No error</u>
     E

8. Charisse missed <u>s</u>chool on <u>W</u>ednesday <u>for the reason that</u> she had to attend her <u>g</u>randfather's funeral. <u>No error</u>
                A   B   C   D   E

9. I <u>have</u> to go shopping today<u>,</u> I <u>need</u> a new jacket<u>__</u> for the job interview. <u>No error</u>
   A   B   C   D   E

10. Marlana <u>hates</u> practicing, <u>and</u> she <u>faithfully</u> does so <u>anyway</u>. <u>No error</u>
           A   B   C   D   E

11. Several student<u>'s</u> cars <u>were</u> damaged <u>in</u> the hailstorms last <u>spring and</u> summer. <u>No error</u>
                A   B   C   D   E

12. The evangelist said<u>,</u> "Do not <u>deceive</u> yourselves<u>,</u> the end is near.<u>"</u> <u>No error</u>
                A   B   C   D E

13. <u>Their</u> <u>are</u> hundreds of <u>sites</u> on the Internet devoted to science fiction <u>texts</u>. <u>No error</u>
      A   B   C   D   E

14. Because he register<u>ed</u> late<u>,</u> there <u>was</u> only one <u>physics</u> 102 class left open. <u>No error</u>
                       A   B   C   D   E

15. An optimist <u>sees</u> the positive side <u>of</u> a situation<u>.</u> While a pessimist focus<u>es</u> on the negative. <u>No error</u>
           A   A   C   D   E

16. The clarinet player was <u>every</u> bit <u>as talented,</u> <u>if not more</u> talented <u>than</u>, the flute player. <u>No error</u>
                        A   B   C   D   E

17. She <u>angrily</u> listed his <u>character</u> <u>flaws selfishness</u>, lack of <u>organization,</u> and laziness. <u>No error</u>
       A   B   C   D   E

18. <u>Because</u> of the <u>proliferation</u> of cellular phones, <u>less</u> people are using pay telephones now compared to <u>ten</u>
   A   B   C   D
years ago. <u>No error</u>
        E

19. Neither the <u>parents</u> nor the child <u>are</u> able <u>to</u> relate <u>well</u> to the counselor. <u>No error</u>
               A   B   C   D   E

20. If you <u>need</u> to find a doctor <u>who</u> you can trust, I can <u>recommend</u> <u>Dr.</u> Leggett. <u>No error</u>
          A   B   C   D   E

21. When my son <u>was</u> in the <u>hospital,</u> his favorite gift <u>was</u> a CD player. <u>No error</u>
              A   B   C   D   E

22. The <u>scholarships</u> <u>go</u> <u>to:</u> Ashley__ and Michelle. <u>No error</u>
     A   B C   D   E

23. Double jeopardy <u>is where</u> <u>an</u> accused defendant__ cannot be__ tried for the same crime twice. <u>No error</u>
                A   B   C   D   E

24. Rock <u>had</u> good intentions, a <u>great</u> intellect, and <u>his leadership ability was well known</u>. <u>No error</u>
      A   B C   D   E

25. Dr<u>.</u> Bell<u>,</u> who has just been hired to teach in the foreign language department<u>,</u> visits <u>Europe</u> every summer.
   A   B   C   D
<u>No error</u>
  E

26. Although I checked__ my gas gauge several times during the trip<u>;</u> I <u>still</u> <u>ran</u> out of gasoline. <u>No error</u>
                 A   B   C   D   E

27. After he <u>lied</u> to his parents<u>,</u> he <u>laid</u> awake all night with his <u>conscience</u> bothering him. <u>No error</u>
              A   B   C   D   E

28. He <u>is</u> one of the boys <u>who</u> <u>was</u> elected to the <u>honor</u> society. <u>No error</u>
     A   B   C   D   E

29. Tom Wolfe<u>'s</u> novel <u>"The Bonfire of the Vanities"</u> was <u>made</u> into a film that <u>starred</u> Tom Hanks. <u>No error</u>
                   A   B   C   D   E

30. If you <u>really</u> wish to know, there are <u>3</u> reasons why <u>I</u> must decline <u>your</u> invitation. <u>No error</u>
        A   B   C   D   E

31. <u>Walking along the beach,</u> the waves <u>looked</u> cool__ and inviting to <u>us</u>. <u>No error</u>
            A   B   C   D   E

32. The <u>principal</u> announced that several <u>Sophomores</u> were <u>given</u> special permission to go on the <u>senior</u> trip.
            A   B   C   D
    <u>No error</u>
        E

33. "What are <u>you</u> trying to say<u>"?</u> she asked <u>him</u> coyly<u>.</u> <u>No error</u>
                A   B   C   D E

34. Last semester the <u>literature</u> students <u>chose</u> <u>"Porphyria's Lover"</u> as <u>their</u> favorite Browning poem. <u>No error</u>
                        A   B   C   C   D   E

35. There <u>is</u> a very strong tradition of <u>women</u>'s basketball__ at the <u>university</u> of Tennessee. <u>No error</u>
            A   B   C   D   E

36. For her birthday<u>,</u> she wanted__ to <u>receive</u> a car from her parents <u>with a sunroof</u>. <u>No error</u>
                        A   B   C   D   E

37. She was making <u>so</u> much money that she <u>had</u> forgotten something real<u>ly</u> important<u>—</u>her dream. <u>No error</u>
                    A   B   C   D   E

38. My <u>c</u>oach and my parents and <u>me</u> <u>are</u> going to ride to the game <u>together</u> on the bus. <u>No error</u>
        A   B   C   D   E

39. <u>Coming home</u> the house <u>was</u> completely dark__ and appear<u>ed</u> empty. <u>No error</u>
        A   B   C   D   E

40. Everyone <u>has</u> to take <u>their</u> shoes off at the door of the <u>Japanese</u> <u>restaurant</u>. <u>No error</u>
                A   B   C   D   E

Directions: Each of the passages below is followed by three questions. Choose the best answer from the options given.

In addition to the well-known physical consequences, cigarette smoking has social consequences. A smoker's clothes and hair reek of smoke, offending and annoying others who must carpool or share an elevator with the smoker. Cigarettes yellow the smoker's teeth, making his or her smile disgusting rather than inviting. The pipe smoker doesn't have this problem. Finally, cigarette smoking causes bad breath that keeps even close friends at a distance.

41. What method of development is used in this passage?

    A.   Classification
    B.   Time order
    C.   Cause and effect
    D.   Definition
    E.   None of the above

42. Which of the following is true of this passage?

    A.   It lacks a topic sentence.
    B.   It contains an irrelevant statement.

C. The word "reek" has neutral connotations.
D. It contains no transition words.
E. None of the above

43. The tone of this passage is

A. critical.
B. humorous.
C. sad.
D. apologetic.
E. None of the above

In the 1950's, Elvis Presley's pompadour gave him a romantic "bad boy" look that made the girls squeal. The Beatles' choirboy hairstyles captured the attention of a public used to the crewcuts of the early 60's, by the end of the decade the Fab Four sported the longer, shaggy look that would be the standard for 70's groups like Kiss. And in the 80's, wild color, such as the bright orange of Cyndi Lauper's hair, was common.

44. Which of the following would be the best topic sentence for this passage?

A. The rock music of today owes much to the early stars.
B. Rock-and-roll musicians have always used gimmicks.
C. Distinctive hairstyles have long been part of the rock-and-roll image.
D. Elvis Presley and the Beatles had much in common.
E. Any of the above

45. What is the writing flaw in this passage?

A. Lack of coherence
B. Lack of unity
C. A comma splice
D. A dangling modifier
E. None of the above

46. In what kind of order are the supporting details of this passage given?

A. Spatial order
B. Cause and effect
C. Time order
D. Order of importance
E. None of the above

Directions: Choose the best option.

47. George Bernard Shaw wrote that to attempt to reform a criminal by putting him in prison was like attempting to cure a person of pneumonia by making him stand outside in the snow all night.

The type of comparison used in the above passage is called

A. a red herring.
B. a hasty generalization.
C. a metaphor.
D. an analogy.
E. None of the above.

48. <u>Whereas</u> the majority of the citizens were interested in adequate health care and more job opportunities.

The underlined word in this sentence should be replaced with

    A.   Whereas,
    B.   However,
    C.   Although
    D.   Whereby
    E.   No change is necessary

49. At the college conference, all professors and their wives as well as all secretaries and their husbands will be invited to a reception.

What is the writing flaw in this sentence?

    A.   Lack of pronoun agreement
    B.   Sexist language
    C.   Faulty predication
    D.   Excessive subordination
    E.   None of the above

50. Even when two people are married, they still should develope some seperate hobbies to keep their relationship intresting.

What is the writing flaw in the preceding sentence?

    A.   Punctuation
    B.   Unnecessary tense shifts
    C.   Misspellings
    D.   Pronoun form
    E.   None of the above

Objective Posttest, Form B

Name_____

1. _____

2. _____

3. _____

4. _____

5. _____

6. _____

7. _____

8. _____

9. _____

10. _____

11. _____

12. _____

13. _____

14. _____

15. _____

16. _____

17. _____

18. _____

19. _____

20. _____

21. _____

22. _____

23. _____

24. _____

25. _____

26. _____

27. _____

28. _____

29. _____

30. _____

31. _____

32. _____

33. _____

34. _____

35. _____

36. _____

37. _____

38. _____

39. _____

40. _____

41. _____

42. _____

43. _____

44. _____

45. _____

46. _____

47. _____

48. _____

49. _____

50. _____

Score _____

Diagnostic Objective Posttest Answer Key, Form B

Question	Answer	*Hodges'* Section	*Writer's* Section
1	D	28c	21e
2	D	21b	30b
3	A	19c	28c
4	B	6a	22e
5	A	5b	21b
6	C	9a	37a
7	E	12	31
8	C	21b	30b
9	B	3a	19a
10	B	24b	24b
11	A	15a	33a
12	C	3a	19a
13	A	18c	36c
14	D	9a	37a
15	C	2	18
16	B	22c	23g
17	C	17d	35d
18	C	19c	28c
19	B	6a	22e
20	B	5c	21c
21	E	12	31
22	C	17d	35d
23	A	23d	23d
24	D	26a	25a
25	E	12d	31d
26	B	14c	32c
27	C	7a	22a
28	C	6a	22e
29	B	10a	38a
30	B	11f	39f
31	A	25b	20f
32	B	9e	37e
33	B	16d	34d
34	E	16b	34b
35	D	9a	37a
36	D	25a	20e
37	E	17e	35e
38	B	5b	21b
39	A	25b	20f
40	B	6b	21d
41	C	31c	2d
42	B	31a	3c
43	A	19a	28a
44	C	31a	3c
45	C	3a	19a
46	C	31c	2d
47	D	20a	29a
48	B	2	18
49	B	19d	28d
50	C	18	36

Diagnostic Essay Test, Form C

Directions: Write an essay on *one* of the following topics. Use standard written English and standard format. (For example, use complete sentences, and observe standard five-space paragraph indentation.)

Suggestions: Allow time at the beginning to plan your essay, perhaps by making a brief outline of the main points that you plan to discuss. Allow some time at the end of the examination period to read what you have written and to make editorial and proofreading changes.

Topics

1. Your psychology class is studying the various and sometimes subtle ways in which parents influence their children. As part of a class project, you have been asked to write an essay in which you analyze the effect some attitude of your mother or father has had in shaping your own ideas and behavior.

2. The American Library Association is asking for help in selecting the one book written in the 20th century that best illustrates, for good or ill, the values and ideas for which 20th-century America will be most remembered. Write a carefully organized essay that nominates the book that you think should be selected.

3. Whether it involves changing a tire or dealing with unpleasant customers, everyone is an expert at some skill. Write an essay explaining how to perform some special skill of yours.

4. In an essay which carefully considers BOTH sides of the issue, argue for or against ONE of these topics: wearing fur, eating meat, hunting for sport.

5. Suppose that your most recent bank balance shows that you need to take better care of your money. In order to give shape to your intention to take charge of your finances, write an essay in which you analyze why you have run into financial difficulty and what you plan to do about it.

6. Accounts of extreme or unusual weather are always newsworthy. Write an essay in which you describe the worst weather you've ever experienced, and explain how you managed to cope with it.

7. Many students have part-time jobs while attending college. Because of your own experience, you have a strong opinion about the advisability of part-time work. Write an essay in which you argue for or against having college students work part-time.

8. Many very old TV shows—such as *The Honeymooners* and *The Andy Griffith Show*—are still quite popular in reruns. Analyze the reasons for the continuing appeal of one of these old TV shows.

Name_____

Date_____

_____

_____

_____

_____

_____

_____

_____

_____

_____

_____

_____

_____

_____

_____

_____

_____

_____

_____

_____

_____

_____

_____

Diagnostic Objective Test, Form C

Directions: Each of the numbered sentences in this test component has five underlined sections. If one of the underlined sections contains an error in standard written English, mark the letter of that section on your answer sheet. No sentence has more than one error, and some sentences may not contain any errors. If there is no error, mark "E" on your answer sheet.

Sample:

Everyone <u>is</u> responsible <u>for</u> <u>their</u> <u>own</u> behavior. <u>No error</u>
　　　　　A　　　　　　　B　　C　　D　　　　　　E

The correct answer is "C." The error is in pronoun agreement because *everyone* is singular but *their* is plural. In *The Hodges' Harbrace Handbook,* this information is found in section 16d.

1.　When Sarah gets out of <u>high</u> school, she wants to go to <u>college</u> and <u>study</u> <u>Chemistry</u>. <u>No error</u>
　　　　　　　　　　　　A　　　　　　　　　　　　　　　B　　　　　C　　D　　　　E

2.　Bill <u>loves</u> to plant <u>flowers;</u> though he <u>dislikes</u> mowing the lawn__ on weekends. <u>No error</u>
　　　　　A　　　　　　B　　　　　　　　C　　　　　　　　　　　D　　　　　　　E

3.　Our teacher ask<u>ed</u> <u>if we had a good time</u> at the <u>museum</u> and <u>didn't we want</u> to go again. <u>No error</u>
　　　　　　　　　　A　B　　　　　　　　　　　　C　　　　　D　　　　　　　　　　E

4.　The actors practic<u>ed</u> late <u>every</u> night this week__ and are <u>so</u> tired. <u>No error</u>
　　　　　　　　　　　A　　　　B　　　　　　　　C　　　　　D　　　E

5.　When she turned thirty<u>-</u>three, she <u>drove</u> back to the farm <u>in</u> which she <u>grew</u> up. <u>No error</u>
　　　　　　　　　　　　A　　　　　　B　　　　　　　　　　C　　　　　　D　　　E

6.　Women<u>'s</u> <u>colleges</u> <u>have</u> remained popular in the <u>eastern</u> United States. <u>No error</u>
　　　A B　　C　　　　　　　　　　　　　　D　　　　　　　　　　E

7.　<u>When buying a computer</u>, a good idea is <u>to</u> compare prices__ and service contracts__ from several
　　　　　A　　　　　　　　　　　　　　B　　　　　　C　　　　　　　　　　D
companies. <u>No error</u>
　　　　　E

8.　Frederico told me that__ his <u>father</u> <u>was</u> born in Montevideo, Uruguay__ in 1950. <u>No error</u>
　　　　　　　　　　A　　B　　C　　　　　　　　　　　　　D　　　　　　　E

9.　Lena asked<u>,</u> "<u>who</u> is the main character in *The Scarlet Letter* <u>?"</u> <u>No error</u>
　　　　　　　A　B　　　　　　　　　　　　　　　　　CD　　E

10.　Before the week<u>'s</u> trip was over<u>,</u> we were all tired of <u>him</u> <u>whining</u>. <u>No error</u>
　　　　　　　　A　　　　　　　B　　　　　　　　　C　　D　　　E

11.　Jason <u>uses</u> his microwave__ to make popcorn__ and <u>for heating</u> up water. <u>No error</u>
　　　　　A　　　　　　B　　　　　　　C　　　　　D　　　　　　　E

12.　In Shakespeare<u>'s</u> play__ *Hamlet*<u>,</u> Ophelia <u>went</u> insane. <u>No error</u>
　　　　　　　A　　　B　　　　　C　　　　　D　　　　　E

13.　Patricia spent her week in Venice__ sightseeing in the <u>museums</u>, boating__ on the canals, and <u>to visit</u> the
　　　　　　　　　　　　　　　A　　　　　　　　B　　　　　C　　　　　　　　　　　D

glass shops. <u>No error</u>
                  E

14. The U.S.S. *Nimitz* figured <u>prominently</u> in the <u>1984</u> film entitled <u>*The Philadelphia Experiment*</u>. <u>No error</u>
         A   B   C   D   E

15. The soccer coach called <u>an</u> end <u>to</u> practice <u>since</u> it was <u>fixing</u> to get dark. <u>No error</u>
                            A   B   C   D   E

16. <u>It's</u> true<u>;</u> a car will stop faster at zero than at <u>thirty-two</u> degrees<u>",</u> said Todd. <u>No error</u>
    A   B   C   D   E

17. I can count on one hand<u>__</u> the people <u>who</u> <u>have been</u> here longer than <u>me</u>. <u>No error</u>
                          A   B   C   D   E

18. I was <u>so</u> upset that I <u>almost ate</u> the whole box of <u>Girl Scout</u> cookies<u>__</u> before I realized what I was doing.
          A   B   C   D
    <u>No error</u>
        E

19. A person who wants to help <u>their</u> community<u>__</u> is often involved in organizations such as<u>__</u> Habitat for
                              A   B   C
    Humanity<u>__</u> and the Red Cross. <u>No error</u>
            D   E

20. "Are you going home for the weekend<u>?"</u> Antonio asked<u>,</u> "I hope <u>you will</u> try to come back early." <u>No error</u>
                                    AB   C   D   E

21. There <u>is</u> a big rocking chair<u>__</u> and an <u>old-fashioned</u> swing on my <u>grandmother's</u> front porch. <u>No error</u>
          A   B   C   D   E

22. <u>Even though</u> John was the <u>youngest</u> of the two boys<u>,</u> he was the one who assumed responsibility for the
    A   B   C
    family after his <u>father's</u> death. <u>No error</u>
                    D   E

23. Neither the members of the tennis team<u>__</u> nor their coach, Mike Blair, <u>were</u> happy with the outcome of the
                                        A   B   C D
    competition. <u>No error</u>
                    E

24. Henry<u>,</u> as well as Don<u>,</u> <u>have</u> not <u>received</u> sufficient recognition for helping to make the campaign a success.
         A   B C   D
    <u>No error</u>
        E

25. Putting on an old<u>__</u> worn-out sweater<u>__</u> and a pair of <u>jeans,</u> Cathy declared <u>herself</u> ready to go. <u>No error</u>
                    A   B   C   D   E

26. "If no one was at <u>home, who</u> did you deliver the picture to<u>?"</u> he ask<u>ed</u>. <u>No error</u>
                    A B   C   D   E

27. Seetha is <u>suppose</u> to call us as soon as she gets home<u>__</u> so we can be sure she gets <u>there</u> <u>safely</u>. <u>No error</u>
              A   B   C   D   E

42   Copyright © Heinle

28. Shawn, unlike Sam, usually walks very fast and takes long, determined strides. No error
    A   B   C   D   E

29. Steve and his wife, Collette, remodeled the house that belonged to the Westons__ and have been living
                        A   B   C

    there about a year. No error
    D   E

30. "Between you and I," he said in a hoarse whisper, "I hope the amendment fails." No error
                       A   B   C   D   E

31. On Tuesdays, I have English in the new annex and History in Franklin Hall. No error
        A   B   C   D   E

32. In order to succeed in the coming year, your company is going to have to cut costs, and increase sales.
                                            A B   C   D

    No error
    E

33. Charles's , parents were angry because of him playing his music loudly, so that they grounded him for a
            A   B   C   D

    week. No error
          E

34. The debate over school uniforms was heated, however, the vote showed an overwhelming majority of
                                              A   B

    parents, teachers, and administrators in favor of them. No error
    C   D   E

35. Don't never think you have repeated a customer's order too often. No error
         A   B   C   D   E

36. There are many reasons I like courses that incorporate new computer technology. For example, online
    A   B   C   D

    lectures and discussion groups. No error
                                    E

37. On Sunday mornings, Henry like to get up early__ and fix a big, hearty breakfast for his family. No error
                              A   B   C   D   E

38. This will be the sixth workshop I've had to attend this year, and, so far, each one has created the same
                                                                A   B

    effect ; long days, bad attitudes, and short tempers. No error
    C   D   E

39. After mowing the lawn, Paul picked up the jug of lemonade__ and didn't quit drinking until he had drank
                          A   B   C   D

    all of it. No error
              E

40. We three—Mary, Gene, and I—are planning to see a movie after Thursday's meeting. If we get out in time.
    A   B   C   D
    No error
    E

Directions : Each of the following passages is followed by a question and five answers. Choose the best answer for each question.

41. My interest in crop dusting began in 1995 when I worked for one. Since then, I have gone on to get my pilot's license.

    What is the flaw in the preceding sentences?

    A. Misspelling
    B. Broad or implied pronoun reference
    C. Unnecessary shift in tense
    D. Unnecessary shift in mood
    E. None of the above

42. When the building was ignited by an arsonist, an alarm was called in by a witness. Although in only a few minutes the blaze was doused by the fire department, already a lot of damage had been caused by the smoke.

    What is the flaw in the preceding sentences?

    A. Comma splices
    B. Slang
    C. Capitalization
    D. Excessive passive voice
    E. None of the above

43. Jim is well-known and well-liked throughout the state; therefore, he cannot fail to make a good college president.

    What is the logical flaw in this sentence?

    A. Ad hominem
    B. Nonsequitur
    C. Bandwagon
    D. Hasty generalization
    E. None of the above

44. The most memorable time I had while on the United States soccer team occurred when we were playing Argentina in a scrimmage, and we were the underdog for the whole tournament, but close to the end of the game, we found ourselves tied one to one.

    What is the flaw in this sentence?

    A. Dangling modifiers and misplaced parts
    B. Ineffective use of the passive voice
    C. Lack of parallelism
    D. Loose, stringy compound sentences
    E. None of the above

45. At 2:00 PM he skipped Mr. Young's senior math class to wash his car so it would be clean for his date. That evening after he picked up Janet, he drove to the movie theater. As he tried to squeeze past someone to get to a seat, he realized with shock that it was Mr. Young.

    What is the main pattern of organization in this passage?

    A. Order of emphasis
    B. Time order

C.   Question-answer pattern
D.   General to specific
E.   None of the above

46. I sighed with relief when Ross told Andy his watch was twenty minutes fast.

What is the flaw in the preceding sentence?

A.   Unnecessary shift in mood
B.   Lack of a clear pronoun antecedent
C.   Faulty predication
D.   Shift between direct and indirect discourse
E.   None of the above

47. Sally laughed, cried, and was hiccupping all at once.

What is the flaw in the preceding sentence?

A.   Ineffective use of the passive voice
B.   Faulty predication
C.   Faulty parallelism
D.   Unnecessary shift in voice
E.   None of the above

48. She was as exacting as a drill sergeant doing a quarter test.

What figure of speech is used in the preceding sentence?

A.   Overstatement
B.   Simile
C.   Metaphor
D.   Personification
E.   None of the above

49. When only a baby, my mother took me to work with her each day and kept me by her side in a basket.

What is the flaw in the preceding sentence?

A.   Lack of parallelism
B.   Unnecessary shift in person
C.   Dangling elliptical clause
D.   Ineffective use of the passive voice
E.   None of the above

50. The reason I missed class is because the alarm didn't go off.

What is the flaw in the preceding sentence?

A.   Faulty or illogical construction
B.   Unnecessary shift in mood
C.   Lack of consistent perspective and viewpoint
D.   Excessive subordination
E.   None of the above

Diagnostic Objective Test, Form C

Name_____

Date_____

1. _____

2. _____

3. _____

4. _____

5. _____

6. _____

7. _____

8. _____

9. _____

10. _____

11. _____

12. _____

13. _____

14. _____

15. _____

16. _____

17. _____

18. _____

19. _____

20. _____

21. _____

22. _____

23. _____

24. _____

25. _____

26. _____

27. _____

28. _____

29. _____

30. _____

31. _____

32. _____

33. _____

34. _____

35. _____

36. _____

37. _____

38. _____

39. _____

40. _____

41. _____

42. _____

43. _____

44. _____

45. _____

46. _____

47. _____

48. _____

49. _____

50. _____

Score _____

Diagnostic Objective Test Answer Key, Form C

Question	Answer	Hodges' Section	Writer's Section
1	D	9e	37e
2	B	14c	32c
3	D	27c	N/A
4	D	22c	23h
5	C	19c	28c
6	E	15a	33a
7	A	25b	20f
8	D	N/A	N/A
9	B	9d	37d
10	C	5c	21c
11	D	26a	25a
12	D	42e	13f
13	D	26a	25a
14	E	10	38
15	D	19c	28c
16	D	16d	34d
17	D	5c	21c
18	B	25a	20e
19	A	6b	21d
20	C	3a	19a
21	A	6a	22e
22	B	4c	20c
23	D	6a	22e
24	C	6a	22e
25	A	12c	31c
26	B	5c	21c
27	A	18b	36b
28	E	12	31
29	E	12	31
30	A	5b	21b
31	D	9e	37e
32	C	13a	31g
33	C	5c	21c
34	A	3a	19a
35	A	4e	20g
36	C	2	18
37	B	6a	22e
38	C	17d	35d
39	D	7a	22a
40	D	2	18
41	B	28c	21e
42	D	29d	26d
43	B	35f	7i
44	D	24b	24b
45	B	31c	2d
46	B	28a	21e
47	C	26a	25a
48	B	20a	29a
49	C	25a	20e
50	A	23d	23d

Essay Posttest, Form C

Directions: Write an essay on *one* of the following topics. Use standard written English and standard format. (For example, use complete sentences, and observe standard five-space paragraph indentation.)

Suggestions: Allow time at the beginning to plan your essay, perhaps by making a brief outline of the main points that you plan to discuss. Allow some time at the end of the examination period to read what you have written and to make editorial and proofreading changes.

Topics

1. Someone has been hired to do a job that you do now or that you have done in the past. Your employer has asked you to write a letter to this new employee, explaining how the job should be done. Your employer has asked you to include those tips and techniques that have made your own performance so exceptional.

2. Identify a children's television show or film, and write an essay describing and analyzing the content, the characters, and themes of the show, as well as the assumptions it makes about its viewers. Explain how you think these various aspects of the show will influence children for better or worse.

3. Lately, stress has caused you to be so tense and irritable that you realize you must do something to help relieve your stress. In order to get started, write an essay analyzing why you are stressed out and what you can do to alleviate stress in the future.

4. Babysitting is often recommended as a good "beginning" job for young people. Based on your own and your friends' experiences, assess the difficulties, dangers, and rewards of babysitting in order to either recommend it or not recommend it as a good job for young people.

5. You have won a free two-year subscription to the magazine of your choice. Identify the magazine you choose as your prize, and explain what led you to make that particular choice.

6. Almost all families have a collection of stories that are repeated whenever gatherings bring everyone together. Because you want to be sure your family stories are passed on to the next generation exactly as they were told, you decide to write an account of a particular family member telling one of the best of these family stories. Write the account as you recall it.

7. You are a consumer who has definite opinions and preferences about everything you buy. Recently, you have learned that a local store is going to quit carrying one of your favorite products. In a letter arguing that the product is the best of its kind by comparing and contrasting it with other similar brands or varieties, try to convince the store manager to reconsider.

8. For an issue of *Education Today,* write an essay on the one or more ways in which you find your education lacking. Explain why it is lacking—what you should have been taught—and what the cost of your miseducation has been.

Essay Posttest, Form C   Answer Sheet

Name_____   Date_____

_____

_____

_____

_____

_____

_____

_____

_____

_____

_____

_____

_____

_____

_____

_____

_____

_____

_____

_____

_____

_____

Objective Posttest, Form C

Directions: Each of the numbered sentences in this test component has five underlined sections. If one of the underlined sections contains an error in standard written English, mark the letter of that section on your answer sheet. No sentence has more than one error, and some sentences may not contain any errors. If there is no error, mark "E" on your answer sheet.

Sample:

Everyone is responsible for their own behavior. No error
     A   B   C   D   E

The correct answer is "C." The error is in pronoun agreement because *everyone* is singular but *their* is plural. In *The Hodges' Harbrace Handbook,* this information is found in section 16d.

1. Her interest and concern for the rights of women continue. No error
          A   B   C   D   E

2. The only eyewitnesses who saw Booth supposedly shot was Federal soldiers. No error
    A   B   C   D   E

3. Students would rather chose where they sit than be assigned seats. No error
     A   B   C   D   E

4. Please lay the dress carefully on the bed so it will not get wrinkled. No error
       A   B   C   D   E

5. Eventhough Tara did not like to swim the backstroke, she always came in first. No error
    A   B   C   D   E

6. Birth order is certainly important in shaping personality__but__gender is perhaps even more__important.
                                   A   B   C   D
  No error
    E

7. "Thanks for all of your support," she said, "I appreciate it a lot." No error
                A   B   C   D   E

8. Every time you set out in the sun, you should remember to put on sunblock. No error
     A   B   C D   E

9. Last summer I visited three of my relatives an aunt who lives in Louisville, Kentucky, an uncle who lives in
                          A   B

   Philadelphia, Pennsylvania, and another uncle who lives in Washington, D.C. No error
                 C   D   E

10. The short story__Battle Royal also serves as the first chapter of the novel__ *Invisible Man*__.No error
               A   B   C   D   E

11. I enjoy riding my bike. Especially__on a pretty__summer day when the birds are singing and everybody is
                        A   B   C   D
  outside. No error
        E

12. You think__Karen should <u>lay</u> down and rest<u>,</u> don't you<u>?</u> <u>No error</u>
    A   B   C   D   E

13. Expect to be nervous before <u>your</u> performance<u>,</u> then turn all that energy to <u>your</u> advantage<u>. No error</u>
                                 A   B   C   D   E

14. She bought all the <u>necessary</u> school <u>supplies, such as,</u> <u>notebooks,</u> <u>loose-leaf</u> paper, pencils, and ballpoint pens.
                          A   B   C   D

   <u>No error</u>
     E

15. Tunica, <u>MS,</u> has <u>built</u> so many gambling casinos that it is begin<u>ning</u> to rival Las Vegas, <u>Nevada,</u> as a tourist
          A   B   C   D

   attraction. <u>No error</u>
              E

16. Although__clearly shocked by hearing what she owed<u>,</u> the elderly woman <u>paid</u> the <u>whole</u> bill at once. <u>No error</u>
          A   B   C   D   E

17. "<u>Who's</u> horse is being led off__the track<u>?</u>" Anna asked<u>. No error</u>
    A   B   C   D   E

18. <u>After spending an hour looking at every Valentine in the store,</u> Teresa <u>finally</u> <u>choose</u> what she thought was
                                 A   B   C   D

   the perfect card. <u>No error</u>
                   E

19. For the <u>past</u> three years, the mayor has <u>lain</u> flowers on the memorial to the <u>war</u> <u>veterans</u>. <u>No error</u>
          A   B   C D   E

20. Dale hopes that we <u>will like</u> the new computer software<u>;</u> he <u>says</u> it is <u>real</u> easy to use. <u>No error</u>
                       A   B   C   D   E

21. Eric, along with Joe, <u>bring</u> life to a play__that would otherwise be <u>mediocre at best</u>. <u>No error</u>
                        A   B   C   D   E

22. Billy Bob Thornton is not <u>only</u> an actor<u>,</u> he is also the director of <u>such</u> films as__*All the Pretty Horses*. <u>No error</u>
                              A   B   C   D   E

23. <u>Between</u> the three of <u>them,</u> they had enough change to buy <u>one</u> bag of <u>potato</u> chips. <u>No error</u>
     A   B   C   D   E

24. Although__there have been several good suggestions about what to do with the unexpected funds__the
          A   B

   committee has__yet__to put the question to a vote. <u>No error</u>
              C   D   E

25. Because of the recent remodeling of the <u>theater,</u> <u>which</u> included deepening the stage and enlarging the orchestra
                                               A   B

   pit<u>.</u> This year's productions are better than last <u>year's</u>. <u>No error</u>
    C   D   E

26. Demetria told me that__the issue that <u>interest</u> her the most__is <u>prison</u> reform. <u>No error</u>
                       A   B   C   D   E

27. <u>After looking at the dead bodies,</u> Mr<u>.</u> Christopher said he <u>seen</u> enough <u>to make</u> anyone sick. <u>No error</u>
      A   B   C   D   E

28. Because the last speaker spoke so softl<u>y,</u> I could <u>barely</u> hear her<u>,</u> and almost <u>fell</u> asleep during her presentation.
                                   A   B   C   D

  <u>No error</u>
    E

29. <u>After dropping out of college,</u> Dick <u>only</u> had two choices: he <u>could</u> get a job <u>or</u> join the military. <u>No error</u>
                  A   B   C   D   E

30. <u>According</u> to him, <u>who</u> underestimated <u>who</u>? <u>No error</u>
    A   B   C   D   E

31. While I was driving home from the <u>hospital,</u> a heavy fog rolled <u>in;</u> it was so thick that <u>I couldn't</u> hardly see
                                  A   B   C   D

  the road. <u>No error</u>
          E

32. Carl decided to drop out of school for a semester__and work with his <u>uncle's</u> <u>advertising</u> agency<u>,</u> he said he
                                          A   B   C   D

  needed the money. <u>No error</u>
                E

33. Angela and <u>I</u> <u>were</u> <u>disappointed</u> at <u>him</u> leaving the party so early. <u>No error</u>
          A B   C   D   E

34. Falling into the reflecting pool during my sister's wedding reception was the <u>worse</u> moment of my <u>life,</u>
                                                            A   B

  everybody was nice<u>,</u> but I was thoroughly <u>embarrassed</u>. <u>No error</u>
           C   D   E

35. You are the one who should tell Ben<u>,</u> he <u>will not</u> <u>accept</u> anyone <u>elses</u> report. <u>No error</u>
                                 A   B   C   D   E

36. <u>There</u> <u>was</u> a coffeepot, a saucepan, and <u>an</u> iron skillet__on top of the stove. <u>No error</u>
    A   B   C   D   E

37. After playing <u>only</u> <u>6</u> games, Rhonda <u>injured</u> her <u>ankle seriously</u>. <u>No error</u>
              A B   C   D   E

38. "<u>All right</u>," he said, "because you would <u>of</u> <u>preceded</u> Jenny in line, the front row seat is still <u>yours</u>." <u>No error</u>
     A   B C   D   E

39. When I was a junior in <u>high school,</u> I memorized Robert Frost's__"The Road Not <u>Taken"</u>. <u>No error</u>
                     A   B   C   D E

40. The <u>knights</u> swords were <u>forged</u> <u>from</u> tempered <u>steel,</u> <u>but</u> still they broke. <u>No error</u>
       A   B C   D   E

Directions: Choose the best answer for each question.

41. Which of the following statements would best qualify as a thesis for a persuasive essay?

    A.   Tourism is a thriving industry in Bermuda.
    B.   Flight 19 consisted of five bomber planes on a routine training mission within the Bermuda Triangle.

C.   All five planes disappeared without a trace.
D.   Evidence suggests that the Bermuda Triangle is a mysterious region.
E.   A rescue plane sent to search for Flight 19 exploded.

42. Which one of the following statements is irrelevant and needs to be excluded?

A.   Tourism is a thriving industry in Bermuda.
B.   Flight 19 consisted of five bomber planes on a routine training mission within the Bermuda Triangle.
C.   All five planes disappeared without a trace.
D.   Evidence suggests that the Bermuda Triangle is a mysterious region.
E.   A rescue plane sent to search for Flight 19 exploded.

43. Pam drove her brother Mike, who likes fast cars that have loud motors that roar when the car accelerates quickly, to the store when he needed groceries because he did not have a license after his recent accident, which he claimed was not his fault.

What is the flaw in the preceding sentence?

A.   Excessive plurals
B.   Excessive subordination
C.   Logical fallacies
D.   Unclear pronoun reference
E.   None of the above

44. I love to go walking. I usually walk with one of my good friends. We talk about everything. We try to catch up on all the day's events.

What is the flaw in the preceding sentences?

A.   Broad or implied reference
B.   Lack of parallelism
C.   Lack of sentence variety
D.   Loose, stringy compound sentences
E.   None of the above

45. While taking the exam, the sound of the sirens caused me to lose my concentration.

What is the flaw in the preceding sentence?

A.   Dangling elliptical adverb phrase
B.   Misspelling
C.   Shift between direct and indirect discourse
D.   Unnecessary shift in mood
E.   None of the above

46. I would advise anyone who is planning to go back to school to keep an open mind. If you don't, you will not be able to adapt.

What is the flaw in the preceding sentences?

A.   Misspelling of words that sound alike
B.   Unnecessary shift in voice
C.   Unnecessary shift in person
D.   Dangling elliptical adverb phrase
E.   None of the above

47. Some considered Dexter a bad dude, and some considered him real rad. No one ever dissed him; everyone thought he was awesome.

What is the flaw in the preceding sentences?

A. Misused semicolon
B. Incomplete comparison
C. Logical fallacies
D. Slang
E. None of the above

48. Recent studies believe that the susceptibility to alcoholism is inherited.

What is the flaw in the preceding sentence?

A. Awkward use of a noun as an adjective
B. Unnecessary shift in person
C. Ineffective use of passive voice
D. Faulty predication
E. None of the above

49. A bone graft rejection is when transplanted bone marrow is attacked by the patient's own immune system.

What is the flaw in the preceding sentence?

A. Misspelling
B. Faulty or illogical construction
C. Dangling modifier
D. Broad pronoun reference
E. None of the above

50. For a comprehensive exam, knowing what to study is as important as to know how to study.

What is the flaw in the preceding sentence?

A. Faulty predication
B. Unnecessary shift in mood
C. Lack of parallelism
D. Faulty or excessive subordination
E. None of the above

Objective Posttest, Form C   **Answer Sheet**

Name_____   Date_____

1. _____   20. _____   39. _____

2. _____   21. _____   40. _____

3. _____   22. _____   41. _____

4. _____   23. _____   42. _____

5. _____   24. _____   43. _____

6. _____   25. _____   44. _____

7. _____   26. _____   45. _____

8. _____   27. _____   46. _____

9. _____   28. _____   47. _____

10. _____   29. _____   48. _____

11. _____   30. _____   49. _____

12. _____   31. _____   50. _____

13. _____   32. _____   Score   _____

14. _____   33. _____

15. _____   34. _____

16. _____   35. _____

17. _____   36. _____

18. _____   37. _____

19. _____   38. _____

Diagnostic Objective Posttest Answer Key, Form C

Question	Answer	Hodges' Section	Writer's Section
1	A	22a	23e
2	D	6a	22e
3	B	7a	22a
4	E	7a	22a
5	A	18	36
6	B	12a	31a
7	C	3a	19a
8	B	7a	22a
9	B	17d	35d
10	B	16b	34b
11	A	2	18
12	B	7a	22a
13	B	3a	19a
14	C	13a	31g
15	A	11d	39d
16	B	12b	31b
17	A	18c	36c
18	D	7a	22a
19	B	7a	22a
20	D	4b	20b
21	A	6a	22e
22	B	3a	19a
23	A	19c	28c
24	B	12b	31b
25	C	2	18
26	B	6a	22e
27	C	7a	22a
28	C	13a	31g
29	B	25a	20e
30	D	5c	21c
31	D	4e	20g
32	D	3a	19a
33	D	5c	21c
34	A	4c	20c
35	D	15a	33a
36	B	6a	22e
37	B	11f	39f
38	C	7a	22a
39	D	16d	34d
40	A	15a	33a
41	D	32c	2b
42	A	31a	3c
43	B	24c	24c
44	C	30a	27a
45	A	25a	20e
46	C	27b	N/A
47	D	19c	28c
48	D	23d	23d
49	B	23d	23d
50	C	26a	25a

CLAST-BASED TESTS

Description of Tests

By legislative action in 1979, Florida mandated two educational goals to be implemented by all public colleges and universities. The first goal emphasizes correct placement in college communication and computation courses. To meet this goal, institutions provide entrance assessment and placement testing, and they counsel students to enroll in the right courses to meet the students' needs in developing essential college-level academic skills. To assist the student, Florida public colleges and universities have identified these essential skills in the areas of communication and computation. In the communication area, Florida students must have a basic command of skills involving reading, listening, writing, and speaking standard American English. The second new goal ensures that all students entering their junior year of college have achieved the communication and computation skills necessary for successful completion of upper-division requirements.

The state of Florida measures the achievement of these goals in the College Level Academic Skills Test (CLAST). The test is constructed to measure the communication and computation skills that community college and state university faculty members expect of students completing the sophomore year of college. Its purpose is part of the overall legislative effort in Florida to ensure that students have acquired the skills expected of them by the time they complete their sophomore year.

CLAST includes four subtests: essay, writing, reading, and computation skills. Objective-test items are used to measure reading and computation skills. Both objective items and the essay are used to measure writing skills. The Harbrace CLAST Diagnostic Test Package includes two forms of an essay test based on the essay-writing portion of the CLAST and two forms of a 40-question objective test based on the objective-writing skills portion of the CLAST.

Description of Essay Test

The student has 60 minutes to write and edit an expository or persuasion essay. The completed essay must demonstrate that the writer can accomplish the following:

1. Choose from one of two prompts.

2. Write for a purpose and an audience while adhering to the time limit.

3. Focus the essay through the development of a thesis.

4. Develop the thesis with support that demonstrates (a) an understanding of the differences between generalization and specifics, (b) the ability to arrange the support logically and to unify the material coherently, and (c) an awareness of the selected audience and purpose.

5. Choose words effectively, avoiding wordiness and or inappropriate diction.

6. Use standard sentence structure, avoiding errors related to parallelism, modification, and subordination /coordination and adhering to standard practices of punctuation to eliminate comma splices, fused sentences, and/or fragments.

7. Achieve variety in sentence style.

8. Proofread and revise to maintain clarity and to eliminate non-standard spelling and punctuation as well as errors related to grammar and usage.

Administration of Essay Test

The student is given 60 minutes to complete the state's CLAST essay test. Dictionaries are not permitted. In order to simulate the test, the student using the model in this booklet should have college-ruled notebook paper (at least four pages), a pen, and the CLAST-Based Essay Test, Form A or Form B.

Scoring and Interpretation of Results

Evaluators of the Florida CLAST Essay use holistic scoring, following a set of descriptions (scoring criteria) and sample (benchmark) papers as guides. (Rather than analyzing specific elements, the evaluators base their scores on their total impressions of the writing.) Two evaluators score each essay, and the scores are then combined. The highest possible score is a 12; the lowest is a 2. A cumulative 6 is a passing score. Noncontiguous scores are considered invalid, and a referee (a third reader) adjudicates such papers. Any paper that is judged to be off one of the two assigned prompts receives an "OT" and the paper is not scored.

CLAST Essay Scoring Criteria

Score of 6:   These papers demonstrate that the writers have sophisticated ideas and are capable of nearly polished prose. A strong thesis is carefully supported. Coherently organized details show the writer's superior ability with word choice and sentence structure. Usage errors and/or mechanical flaws are rare.

Score of 5:   These papers contain mature ideas with specific and convincing support for the thesis. Occasionally, errors in mechanics, usage, and/or sentence structure occur; however, the writers maintain control over word choice and use sentence variety.

Score of 4:   These papers contain a thesis and an organizing plan with enough support to accomplish the writer's purpose. Language is used competently and sentence structure sometimes varies. Although errors in mechanics, usage, and/or sentence structure may occur, they do not interfere with communication.

Score of 3:   These papers contain a thesis and an organizing plan; however, the support is often unconvincing due to the use of lists and generalizations. The papers generally lack sentence variety. Errors in mechanics, usage, and/or sentence structure tend to slow the reading.

Score of 2:   These papers usually contain a main idea, but the support is likely to be illogical and inadequate. Simple sentence structure dominates the writing. Errors in mechanics, usage, and/or sentence structure frequently interfere with the reading.

Score of 1:   These papers may lack a thesis or include a main idea that is vague, use support that is general or even rambling, and/or contain numerous errors in usage, mechanics, and sentence structure that disrupt the reading.

Description of English Language Skills Test

The Florida English Language Skills Test covers 16 skills in a 40-item objective test. The 16 skills are as follows:

1.   choosing denotative and connotative words,

2.   avoiding wordiness,

3.   placing modifiers accurately,

4.   using coordination and subordination logically,

5.   maintaining parallelism,

6.   avoiding fragments, comma splices, and fused sentences,

7. using standard forms of verbs,

8. maintaining subject–verb agreement,

9. maintaining pronoun–antecedent agreement,

10. using pronouns in their correct case,

11. using correct adjectives and adverbs,

12. avoiding incorrect shifts in tense,

13. making comparisons logically,

14. using correct spelling,

15. using standard punctuation (commas, semicolons, colons, apostrophes, and quotations), and

16. using standard capitalization.

Administration of English Language Skills Test

The English Language Skills Test and a reading test are combined with 80 minutes allowed for both. A 30-minute period is suggested for the English Language Skills portion and 50 minutes for the reading section. Therefore, when the practice tests from this booklet are given, students should be given approximately 30 minutes. Materials needed to administer the sample ELS Test are a timer, pencils, and either Scantron sheets or answer sheets reproduced from the included sample.

Scoring and Interpretation of Results

A score of 295 (equivalent to 77%) is necessary to pass the Florida English Language Skills Test. Of the 40 items on the test, 35 are scored and 5 are developmental; thus, to pass, a student must have 27 items correct with no penalty for guessing. In administering tests from the Harbrace CLAST Diagnostic Test Package, the instructor should count all 40 questions and set the passing score at 77%.

CLAST-BASED English Language Skills Test, Form A

Directions: The following passage contains several errors. Read the passage. Then answer each test item by choosing the option that corrects an error in the underlined portion (or portions). **Refer to the passage as necessary**. No more than one underlined error will appear in each item. If no error exists, choose "No change is necessary."

In "Life in the Shadows," published in *Discover* in February 1997, Robert W. Marion outlined the medical history of Edwin Rivera. A premature baby whose pediatrician detected some undefined abnormality. Suspecting a liver problem that can be improved with light therapy, physicians placed Edwin under special fluorescent lamps, but the result was blistering wherever light strikes. Within hours, an astute team of doctors diagnosed Edwin as having CEP, or congenital erythropoietic porphyria.

CEP afflicts only a few people throughout the world; nevertheless, from its associated symptoms, medical historians theorize, vampire legends may have come into existence. CEP patients often have a reddish discoloration on their teeth; and their urine tends to be darkened. Furthermore, they cannot be exposed to light, as they lack enzymes necessary to break down toxins. Without a cleansing of the toxins, proteins build up, an extreme reaction occurs. In light, the CEP patients skin blisters severely. Sadly, repeated blistering causes scarring, and patches of hair may grow indiscriminate. One can see how a naïve public in earlier times might of superstitiously viewed such patients as blood drinkers who waited for potential victims in darkness.

While there is currently no simple cures for CEP, some controls are possible. Frequent blood transfusions help alleviate it. A better long-term hope, however, is a transplant with compatible bone marow.

1. In "Life in the Shadows," published in *Discover* in February <u>1997, Robert</u> W. Marion outlined the
    A

   medical history of Edwin <u>Rivera. A premature</u> baby <u>whose</u> pediatrician detected some undefined abnormality.
    B   C

   A. 1997 Robert
   B. Rivera, a premature
   C. who's
   D. No change is necessary.

2. Suspecting a liver problem that can be improved with light therapy, <u>physicians</u> placed Edwin under fluorescent
    A

   <u>lamps, but</u> the result was blistering wherever light <u>strikes.</u>
    B   C

   A. Physicians
   B. lamps but
   C. struck
   D. No change is necessary.

3. Within hours, an astute team of doctors <u>diagnosed</u> Edwin as having CEP, or congenital erythropoietic porphyria.

   A. diagnose
   B. diagnoses
   C. have diagnose
   D. No change is necessary.

4. CEP afflicts only a few people throughout the <u>world; nevertheless,</u> from its associated symptoms, medical
    A

   historians theorize, vampire legends <u>may have come</u> into <u>existance</u>.
    B   C

A. world, nevertheless,
B. may have came
C. existence
D. No change is necessary.

5. CEP patients often have a reddish discoloration on their <u>teeth; and their</u> urine tends to be darkened.

   A. teeth, and their
   B. teeth, their
   C. teeth; and his/her
   D. No change is necessary.

6. Without a cleansing of the toxins, proteins <u>build up, an extreme</u> reaction occurs.

   A. build up, and an extreme
   B. built up, and an extreme
   C. builds up, an extreme
   D. No change is necessary.

7. In light, the CEP <u>patients</u> skin <u>blisters</u> <u>severely</u>.
                       A   B   C

   A. patient's
   B. blistered
   C. severe
   D. No change is necessary.

8. Sadly, repeated blistering <u>causes</u> scarring, and <u>patches</u> of hair may grow <u>indiscriminate</u>.
                           A   B   C

   A. cause
   B. patches'
   C. indiscriminately
   D. No change is necessary.

9. One can see how a naïve public in earlier times <u>might of superstitiously viewed</u> such patients as blood drinkers who waited for potential victims in darkness.

   A. might of superstitiously view
   B. might had superstitiously viewed
   C. might have superstitiously viewed
   D. No change is necessary.

10. While <u>there</u> <u>is</u> currently no simple cures for CEP, some controls are <u>possible</u>.
             A B   C

    A. their
    B. are
    C. posible
    D. No change is necessary.

11. Frequent blood transfusions help alleviate <u>it</u>.

    A. them
    B. the symptoms
    C. your symptoms
    D. No change is necessary.

Directions: Choose the sentence that expresses the thought most clearly and effectively and that has no errors in structure.

12. A. At the movie theatre, the attendants serve popcorn to the customers in huge tubs.
    B. The attendants at the movie theatre serve popcorn to customers in huge tubs.
    C. At the movie theatre, the attendants serve popcorn in huge tubs to customers.

13. A. The holiday was celebrated with great joy, opening presents and eating a huge, calorie-filled meal.
    B. We celebrated the holiday with great joy, opening presents and eating a huge, calorie-filled meal.
    C. Opening presents and eating a huge, calorie-filled meal, the holiday was celebrated with great joy.

14. A. The class appointed a committee, consisting of Kenya and Marcie, who represented the girls, and Jefferson and Daniel, representing the boys.
    B. The class appointed a committee that consisted of Kenya and Marcie as representatives of the girls and Jefferson and Daniel, representing the boys.
    C. The class appointed a committee consisting of Kenya and Marcie, who represented the girls, and Jefferson and Daniel, who represented the boys.

15. A. The neighborhood children would watch television together, play board games like Monopoly, or they would ride their bikes to the nearest playground to shoot a few hoops.
    B. The neighborhood children would watch television together, played board games like Monopoly, or rode their bikes to the nearest playground to shoot a few hoops.
    C. The neighborhood children would watch television together and play board games like Monopoly, or they would ride their bikes to the nearest playground to shoot a few hoops.

16. A. The waiters agreed at the end of the shift to split the tips equally.
    B. At the end of the shift, the waiters agreed to split the tips equally.
    C. The waiters agreed at the end of the shift equally to split the tips.

17. A. When I went to camp, I learned not only about how to build a campfire and how to hold a canoe paddle but also about how to be an independent person.
    B. When I went to camp, I not only learned about building a campfire and holding a canoe paddle but also about being independent.
    C. When I went to camp, I learned to build a campfire, to steer a canoe, and who I was as an independent person.

Directions: Choose the most effective word or phrase within the context suggested by the sentence(s).

18. It is a mark of good breeding to show a little _____ now and then.

    A. bashfulness
    B. timidity
    C. modesty

19. The _____ cheers from the stadium encouraged the team to go for the touchdown.

    A. earnest
    B. fervent
    C. enthusiastic

20. Andrew Carnegie, a major benefactor to libraries and other charities, was a man of great_____.

    A. funds
    B. wealth
    C. abundance

Directions: For the following underlined sentences, choose the option that expresses the meaning with the most fluency and the clearest logic within the context. If the underlined sentences should not be changed, choose option A, which shows no change.

21. <u>Fred Astaire dances with a vacuum cleaner, Alfred Hitchcock wears a nasal strip, and Lucille Ball admires diamonds.</u> What icon of the entertainment world will the advertisers use next?

    A. Fred Astaire dances with a vacuum cleaner, Alfred Hitchcock wears a nasal strip, and Lucille Ball admires diamonds.
    B. When Fred Astaire dances with a vacuum cleaner and Alfred Hitchcock wears a nasal strip, Lucille Ball admires diamonds.
    C. Fred Astaire dances with a vacuum cleaner. Alfred Hitchcock wears a nasal strip. Lucille Ball admires diamonds.
    D. Fred Astaire dances with a vacuum cleaner, and Alfred Hitchcock wears a nasal strip; moreover, Lucille Ball admires diamonds.

22. Over a million boys use chewing tobacco or snuff, and an estimated four and a half million young people smoke 30 billion cigarettes a year. <u>With these facts in mind, no one should be surprised that American consumers who are afflicted with tongue, lip, and lung cancers continue.</u>

    A. With these facts in mind, no one should be surprised that American consumers who are afflicted with tongue, lip, and lung cancers continue.
    B. Having these facts in mind, no one should be surprised that American consumers are afflicted with cancers which occur on the tongue, lip, and lung.
    C. With these facts in mind, no one should be surprised that tongue, lip, and lung cancers continue to afflict American consumers.
    D. However, with these facts in mind, no one should be surprised that American consumers who have tongue, lip, and lung cancers continue to be afflicted.

23. Even though we correctly associate the 1930's with the Great Depression and thus imagine it to have been a period of little progress, some remarkable time-saving devices came on the market during that period. <u>For example, electric stoves appeared, and Birdseye introduced frozen food products.</u>

    A. For example, electric stoves appeared, and Birdseye introduced frozen food products.
    B. Electric stoves appeared whereas Birdseye introduced frozen food products.
    C. Electric stoves, for example, appeared, and, on the other hand, Birdseye introduced frozen food products.
    D. For example, electric stoves appeared, but Birdseye introduced frozen food products.

Directions: The following passage contains several errors. Read the passage. Then answer each test item by choosing the option that corrects an error in the underlined portion (or portions). Refer to the passage as necessary. No more than one underlined error will appear in each item. If no error exists, choose "No change is necessary."

Television sitcoms thrive on the interplay between regulars and guests; consequently, settings with potential for introducing new characters helps a series succeed. *Cheers* and *Barney Miller,* both currently discontinued, illustrate this principle real well. Manhattan South's detective room allowed on-going characters to interact with various victims and criminals. The bar in *Cheers* logically linked Sam Malone and his waitresses with everyone from Carla's ex-husband to Diane's would-be Othello.

Ted Danson's currently running sitcom also demonstrates the importance of a public setting. As Becker, in the series by the same name, Danson plays a doctor into whose office come odd but fasinating patients. Additionally, at Becker's favorite coffee shop, another public setting, even odder personalities—from pickpockets to prostitutes—ignite Becker's considerable ire.

Each show also has their own intimate set, letting viewers glimpse the main character's inner world. In *Becker,* we occasionally visit the doctor's apartment, in *Barney Miller,* we were taken into Barney's *sanctum sanctorum* for debates over police procedure. For sitcom fans, however, no intimate set is as memorable as Cheers' inner office. Where Sam amused us with his attempted seductions.

Are the mix of intimate and public sets necessary for a sitcom's success? One has only to recall *All in the Family,* the top-rated program of the 1970's. Archie Bunker and his family rarely left their living room, yet Americans watched avidly as Archie berated Edith, and bellyached about Meathead. On the other hand, *Seinfeld,* the dominant sitcom of the 1990's, use all of Manhattan as its stage.

24. Television sitcoms thrive on the interplay between regulars and <u>guests; consequently, settings</u> with potential for logically introducing new characters helps a series succeed.

    A. guests; consequently, a setting
    B. guests, consequently, settings
    C. guests; consequently a setting
    D. No change is necessary.

25. *Cheers* and *Barney Miller,* both currently discontinued, <u>illustrate</u> this principle <u>real</u> <u>well</u>.
                                                         A   B   C

    A. illustrates
    B. really
    C. good
    D. No change is necessary.

26. Manhattan South's detective room allowed on-going characters to interact with various victims and <u>criminals.</u>
                                                                                                    A

    <u>The bar</u> in *Cheers* logically <u>linked</u> Sam Malone and his waitresses with <u>everyone from</u> Carla's ex-husband to
                                            B   C

    Diane's would-be Othello.

    A. criminals. While the bar
    B. link
    C. everyone: from
    D. No change is necessary.

27. As Becker, in the series by the same <u>name, Danson</u> plays a doctor into whose office <u>come</u> various odd but
                                                      A   B
    <u>fasinating</u> patients.
        C

    A. name Danson
    B. came
    C. fascinating
    D. No change is necessary.

28. Additionally, at Becker's favorite <u>coffee shop</u>, another public setting, even <u>odder</u> personalities—from
                                                         A   B

    pickpockets to prostitutes—ignite Becker's <u>considerable</u> ire.
                                                       C

    A. Coffee Shop
    B. more odd
    C. considerably
    D. No change is necessary.

64

29. Each show also <u>has their</u> own intimate set, letting viewers glimpse the main character's inner world.

    A. have their
    B. has its
    C. has there
    D. No change is necessary.

30. In *Becker,* we occasionally visit the doctor's <u>apartment, in</u> *Barney Miller,* we were taken into Barney's *sanctum sanctorum* for debates over police procedure.

    A. apartment and in
    B. apartment; in
    C. apartment, also in
    D. No change is necessary.

31. For sitcom fans, however, no intimate set is as memorable as Cheers' inner <u>office. Where Sam</u> amused us with his attempted seductions.

    A. office; where Sam
    B. office, there Sam
    C. office, in which Sam
    D. No change is necessary.

32. <u>Are</u> the mix of intimate and public sets necessary for a <u>sitcom's</u> <u>success</u>?
   A   B   C

    A. Is
    B. sitcoms
    C. sucess
    D. No change is necessary.

33. Archie <u>Bunker and</u> his family rarely left their living <u>room, yet</u> Americans watched avidly as Archie berated
               A   B
<u>Edith, and</u> bellyached about Meathead.
     C

    A. Bunker, and
    B. room yet
    C. Edith and
    D. No change is necessary.

34. On the other hand, *Seinfeld,* the dominant sitcom of the <u>1990's, use</u> all of Manhattan as <u>its</u> stage.

    A. 1990's use
    B. 1990's, used
    C. 1990's used
    D. No change is necessary.

Directions: Choose the underlined word or phrase that is unnecessary in the context of the passage.

35. Even with technology surrounding us <u>in our modern day world</u>, it's <u>still</u> difficult to imagine that a <u>fragile</u> Apollo
                                              A   B   C
butterfly, weighting <u>about</u> one-hundredth of an ounce, <u>could be equipped to</u> carry tiny radar probes.
                          D   E

A. in our modern day world
B. still
C. fragile
D. about
E. could be equipped to

36. In the <u>musical</u> *Chicago,* except for one or two <u>slight</u> missteps, the male and female ensemble <u>of ten</u> danced
             A   B   C
together in <u>excellent</u> rhythm <u>with each other</u>.
           D   E

A. musical
B. slight
C. of ten
D. excellent
E. with each other

37. While waiting for my car <u>to be repaired</u>, I overheard the <u>service</u> personnel converse <u>back and forth</u> about their
                                  A   B   C
Saturday night dates, their plans for dinner, and their frustrations <u>with the boss</u>. I wondered if I would be
                                                               D
charged <u>for the time</u> they were spending on this conversation.
          E

A. to be repaired
B. service
C. back and forth
D. with the boss
E. for the time

Directions: Choose the sentence that logically and correctly expresses the comparison.

38. A. Denzel Washington is as handsome, if not more handsome than, Laurence Fishburne.
    B. Denzel Washington is as handsome as, if not more handsome than, Laurence Fishburne.
    C. Denzel Washington is handsome as, if not more handsome than, Laurence Fishburne.

39. A. Janelle's talent at computers is greater than her twin's.
    B. Janelle's talent at computers is greater than her twin.
    C. Janelle's talent at computers is greater than is her twin.

40. A. The coach warned the players that taking steroids could be as dangerous to their long-term health as using
        any other drug.
    B. The coach warned the players that taking steroids could be more dangerous to their long-term health.
    C. The coach warned the players that taking steroids could be as dangerous to their long-term health, if not
        more than, using other drugs.

66

CLAST-Based Objective Test, Form A

Answer Sheet

Name_____

Date _____

1. _____

2. _____

3. _____

4. _____

5. _____

6. _____

7. _____

8. _____

9. _____

10. _____

11. _____

12. _____

13. _____

14. _____

15. _____

16. _____

17. _____

18. _____

19. _____

20. _____

21. _____

22. _____

23. _____

24. _____

25. _____

26. _____

27. _____

28. _____

29. _____

30. _____

31. _____

32. _____

33. _____

34. _____

35. _____

36. _____

37. _____

38. _____

39. _____

40. _____

Score _____

CLAST-Based Objective Test Answer Key and Correction Chart, Form A

Question	Answer	*Hodges'* Section	*Writer's* Section
1	B	2	18
2	C	27a	N/A
3	D	7a	22a
4	C	18	36
5	A	14c	32c
6	A	3a	19a
7	A	15a	33a
8	C	4b	20b
9	C	7a	22a
10	B	6a	22e
11	B	28a	21e
12	C	25a	20e
13	B	25b	20f
14	C	26a	25a
15	C	26a	25a
16	B	25a	20e
17	A	26a	25a
18	C	20a	29a
19	C	20a	29a
20	B	20a	29a
21	A	24b	24b
22	C	23d	23d
23	A	24b	24b
24	A	6a	22e
25	B	4b	20b
26	D	2	18
27	C	18	36
28	D	4b	20b
29	B	6b	21d
30	B	3a	19a
31	C	2	18
32	A	6a	22e
33	C	13	31g
34	B	7a	22a
35	A	21b	23a
36	E	21b	30b
37	C	21b	30b
38	B	22c	23h
39	A	22c	23h
40	A	22c	23h

CLAST-Based Essay Test, Form A

Directions for the Essay: You have an hour to compose an expository or a persuasive essay in response to **one** of the following topics:

Topic one: a place that holds particularly positive memories for you

---

or

Topic two: a particular institution's policy, rule, or practice that should be reformed or eliminated

---

After you have selected your topic, be sure that:

- you fully and logically address the topic,

- you support your ideas with concrete and convincing details,

- your approach remains coherent and unified,

- you choose appropriate and effective words, and

- you avoid errors of punctuation, capitalization, spelling, and/or syntax.

Remember to think and plan before you write and to save time to proofread. The reader (teacher or test scorer) will not penalize you for handwriting, but please write legibly to allow the evaluator(s) to judge the paper's content fairly. Add or neatly cross out information if necessary.

Use the following pages for your planning and final copy. Since any "brainstorming" or outlining that you do will not be used to score your paper, mark through such material so that the evaluator may clearly see where your essay begins.

CLAST-Based Essay Test, Form A Answer Sheet

Name_____   Date_____

_____

_____

_____

_____

_____

_____

_____

_____

_____

_____

_____

_____

_____

_____

_____

_____

_____

_____

_____

_____

_____

_____

70

CLAST-Based English Language
Skills Test, Form B

Directions: The following passage contains several errors. Read the passage. Then answer each test item by choosing the option that corrects an error in the underlined portion (or portions). **Refer to the passage as necessary**. No more than one underlined error will appear in each item. If no error exists, choose "No change is necessary."

In his huge book *The Fifties,* author David Halberstam describes an era he sees as filled with dramatic changes that continues to affect our lives today. One of the most remarkable changes was in the places the American people live. Americans used to live on farms and cities, today, they live primarily in suburbs. The person most responsible for our move to the suburbs, says Halberstam, might have been William Levitt, the genius behind Levittown. Shortly after World War II, he created a town out of vacant land. A 17,000-home development, still the worlds's largest, on what had once been a potato farm on Long Island.

He applied mass-production techniques to home building, but instead of moving the houses, they moved the workers from house to house. Each worker was highly specialized and performed only a few operations. One workers task was just to bolt washing machines to the floor. Another worker might, for example, only do window trimming. To keep costs down, Levitt buys tracts of forest, a sawmill, a nail factory, a building-supply store, earthmoving equipment, and concrete mixers. To make building even faster and easier for his carpenters, he made only one basic model house, many parts of which could be precut to the right length, preassembled, and trucked to the sight to be bolted together. Although the houses all tended to look identical, they were extremely well built and low priced. All 17,000 were sold in a little over four years. Clearly, Levitt had found a need for low-cost housing and an efficient way to satisfy that need.

1. In his huge book *The Fifties,* author David Halberstam describes <u>an era he sees as filled</u> <u>with dramatic changes</u>

                                                A   A

   that <u>continues</u> to <u>affect</u> our lives today.
        B   C

   A. "an era he sees as filled with dramatic changes"
   B. continue
   C. effect
   D. No change is necessary.

2. One of the most remarkable changes was in the places the <u>American</u> people live. Americans used to live on
                                                  A

   <u>farms and</u> in <u>cities, today,</u> they live primarily in suburbs.
     B   C

   A. american
   B. farms, and
   C. cities; today,
   D. No change in necessary.

3. The person most responsible for our move to the suburbs, says <u>Halberstam, might have been</u> William Levitt, the genius behind Levittown.

   A. Halberstam, could of been
   B. Halberstam; might have been
   C. Halberstam might have been
   D. No change is necessary.

71

Copyright © Heinle

4. Shortly after <u>World War II, he</u> created a town out of vacant <u>land. A</u> 17,000-home development, still the world's
                     A   B

    largest, on what <u>had once been</u> a potato farm on Long Island.
                            C

    A. World War II he
    B. land, a
    C. use to be
    D. No change is necessary.

5. He <u>applied</u> mass-production techniques to home <u>building, but</u> instead of moving the houses, <u>they</u> moved the
          A   B   C

    workers from house to house.

    A. applies
    B. building; but
    C. Levitt
    D. No change is necessary.

6. Each worker was highly <u>specialized and performed</u> only a few operations.

    A. specialized and performs
    B. specialized and had performed
    C. specialized, and performed
    D. No change is necessary.

7. One <u>workers</u> task <u>was</u> just to bolt washing machines to the floor. Another worker <u>might, for example,</u> only do
            A   B   C   C

    window trimming.

    A. worker's
    B. is
    C. might; for example.
    D. No change is necessary.

8. To keep costs down, <u>Levitt buys tracts</u> of forest, a sawmill, a nail factory, a building-supply store, earth-moving
    equipment, and concrete mixers.

    A. Levitt buys: tracts
    B. Levitt bought tracts
    C. Levitt bought: tracts
    D. No change is necessary.

9. To make building even faster and easier for <u>his carpenters</u>, he made only one basic model <u>house, many</u> parts of
                                         A   B

    which could be precut to the right length, preassembled, and trucked to the <u>sight</u> to be bolted together.
                                                                       C

    A. their carpenters
    B. house. Many
    C. site
    D. No change is necessary.

10. Although the houses all <u>tended</u> to look <u>identical</u>, they were extremely well built and low priced. All 17,000 <u>were</u>
                               A   B   C
sold in a little over four years.

    A. tend
    B. identically
    C. was
    D. No change is necessary.

11. Clearly, Levitt <u>had found</u> <u>a need</u> for low-cost housing and an <u>efficient</u> way to satisfy that need.
                            A   B   C

    A. had founded
    B. their need
    C. efficient
    D. No change is necessary.

Directions: Choose the sentence that expresses the thought most clearly and effectively and that has no errors in structure.

12. A. To help prevent osteoporosis, women should lift weights, as well as take calcium supplements or eat calcium-rich vegetables.
    B. By lifting weights, as well as eating calcium-rich vegetables or taking calcium supplements, osteoporosis can be prevented.
    C. When preventing osteoporosis, it helps to eat calcium-rich vegetables or to take calcium supplements, as well as to lift weights.

13. A. One bicycle may be better than its competitor because of where the bike is made, the quality of materials that are used to make it, and the procedures by which the bike is made.
    B. One bicycle may be better than its competitor because of where and how it's made as well as because of the materials used to make it.
    C. One bicycle may be better than its competitor because of where the bike is made and the materials and process used to make it.

14. A. To become an expert but budget-conscious host, estimate the number of guests, decide on the menu, and watch for sales on party supplies and menu items.
    B. To become an expert but budget-conscious host, estimate how many guests you will have, what your menu will be, and then you can watch for sales on party supplies and menu items.
    C. To become an expert but budget-conscious host, decide whom you will invite, what your menu will be, and then you can watch for sales on party supplies as well as menu items.

15. A. Maida is a heavy-metal music lover and who also enjoys listening to folk songs.
    B. Maida loves to listen to both folk songs and heavy-metal music.
    C. Maida listens to both folk songs and enjoys heavy-metal too.

16. A. Turning cartwheels, Merri Lee's ankle was badly injured.
    B. Merri Lee's ankle was badly injured while turning cartwheels.
    C. Merri Lee badly injured her ankle while she was turning cartwheels.

17. A. The teacher agreed during the next class to help the students with the assignment that was giving them trouble.
    B. The teacher making the troublesome assignment agreed during the next class to help the students complete it.
    C. During the next class, the teacher agreed to help the students complete the assignment that was giving them trouble.

Directions: Choose the most effective word or phrase within the context suggested by the sentence.

18. The _____ attitude of his team encouraged the coach to hope for success.

    A. dogged
    B. obstinate
    C. inflexible

19. The metaphysical poets of the seventeenth century were admired for their use of _____.

    A. embellishment
    B. overstatement
    C. bombast

20. The students were so _____ with their work at the computer terminals that they did not notice the fire alarm.

    A. enamored
    B. enraptured
    C. absorbed

Directions: For the underlined sentences, choose the option that expresses the meaning with the most fluency and the clearest logic within the context. If the underlined sentences should not be changed, choose option A, which shows no change.

21. Scientists estimate that among asteroids one or more kilometers in diameter, about two thousand asteroids cross earth's orbit. <u>Because only about ten percent of them have been cata-logued, a strike on our planet by any one asteroid could cause devastating tidal waves or cataclysmic climate changes.</u>

    A. Because only about ten percent of them have been catalogued, a strike on our planet by any asteroid could cause devastating tidal waves or cataclysmic climate changes.
    B. Only about ten percent of them have been catalogued, and a strike on our planet by any asteroid could cause devastating tidal waves or cataclysmic climate changes.
    C. Only about ten percent of them have been catalogued; however, if any asteroid struck our planet, it could cause devastating tidal waves or cataclysmic climate changes.
    D. Only about ten percent of them have been catalogued, and devastating tidal waves or cataclysmic climate changes could result if any asteroid struck our planet.

22. <u>As a weasel is ideally suited for killing small rodents, it has short legs, a long, thin body, and powerful jaws which enable it to invade an underground burrow. There it quickly slays a mouse, its favorite prey.</u>

    A. As a weasel is ideally suited for killing small rodents, it has short legs, a thin body, and powerful jaws which enable it to invade an underground burrow. There it quickly slays a mouse, its favorite prey.
    B. A weasel is ideally suited for killing small rodents since it has short legs, a thin body, and powerful jaws which enable it to invade an underground burrow where it quickly slays a mouse which is its favorite prey.
    C. A weasel, which is ideally suited for killing small rodents, has short legs, a thin body, and powerful jaws, and these features enable it to invade an underground burrow. There it quickly slays a mouse, its favorite prey.
    D. A weasel is ideally suited for killing small rodents. The weasel's short legs, thin body, and powerful jaws enable it to invade an underground burrow and quickly slay a mouse, its favorite prey.

23. Eating utensils have an interesting history. <u>The common dinner fork, for example, was used in Turkey from the 6th to the 3rd millennium BC but then seems to have disappeared but returned to use in the 14th century AD.</u>

    A. The common dinner fork, for example, was used in Turkey from the 6th to the 3rd millennium BC but then seems to have disappeared but returned to use in the 14th century AD.
    B. For example, the common dinner fork, which was used in Turkey from the 6th to the 3rd millennium BC, seems to have disappeared; on the other hand, it returned to use in the 14th century AD.
    C. An example is the common dinner fork. It was used in Turkey from the 6th to the 3rd millennium BC. Then it seems to have disappeared. It finally returned to use in the 14th century AD.
    D. The common dinner fork, for example, was used in Turkey from the 6th to the 3rd millennium BC but then seems to have disappeared before finally returning to use in the 14th century AD.

Directions: The following passage contains several errors. Read the passage. Then answer each test item by choosing the option that corrects an error in the underlined portion (or portions). **Refer to the passage as necessary**. No more than one underlined error will appear in each item. If no error exists, choose "No change is necessary."

One of the more sad events in the history of comics occurred with the retirement of Bill Watterson, creator of the *Calvin and Hobbes* strip. He was the small boy, presumably a first-grader, who epitomized imagination and energy, both harnessed in the creation of destruction. Calvin was accompanied by the following characters. His parents, Susie, Ms. Wormwood, Moe, Rosalyn, and—more importantly—Hobbes.

The product of Calvin's imagination, Hobbes was a stuffed tiger. When other kids or an adult was present, Hobbes was just a small, limp toy; but when him and Calvin were alone, Hobbes became larger than Calvin, a willing coconspirator and sometime opponent. He was the imaginary friend carried to a higher and infinitely more intresting plane.

With Hobbes as his cohort, the destructive Calvin could victimize his babysitter, Rosalyn. He might lock her out of the house or, worse, calls her boyfriend. When Hobbes was at his side, the insecure Calvin could ask unanswerable questions about the universe or express his fear that sometimes the world was "a pretty mean place." Sometimes it **was** mean, Moe, the school bully, extorted quarters from Calvin or just beat him up for no reason, for instance.

At least the end of Calvin and Hobbes offer peace to the child's beleaguered mother and father and to his teacher, Ms. Wormwood. Faithful readers, though, would certainly be pleased to see more of the devilish Calvin, and not just on the rear end of a truck!

24. One of the <u>more</u> sad events in the history of comics <u>occurred</u> with the retirement of Bill <u>Watterson, creator</u> of the
                A   B   C
Calvin and Hobbes strip.

    A. saddest
    B. occured
    C. Watterson; creator
    D. No change is necessary.

25. <u>He</u> was the small boy, presumably a <u>first-grader</u>, who epitomized imagination and energy, both <u>harnessed</u> in
   A   B   C
the creation of destruction.

    A. Calvin
    B. First-grader
    C. harness
    D. No change is necessary.

26. Calvin was accompanied by the following <u>characters. His</u> parents, Susie, Ms. Wormword, Moe, Rosalyn, and—more importantly—Hobbes.

    A. characters; his
    B. charaters; his
    C. characters: his
    D. No change is necessary.

27. Hobbes, the product of <u>Calvin's imagination was</u> a stuffed tiger.

    A. Calvins' imagination was
    B. Calvins' imagination, was
    C. Calvin's imagination, was
    D. No change is necessary.

28. When other kids or an adult was present, Hobbes was just a small, limp toy; but when <u>him and Calvin</u> were alone, Hobbes became larger than Calvin, a willing coconspirator and sometime opponent.

    A. Calvin and him
    B. Calvin and himself
    C. the two
    D. No change is necessary.

29. He was the imaginary friend carried to a <u>higher and</u> infinitely more <u>intresting</u> <u>plane</u>.
                                A   B   C

    A. higher, and
    B. interesting
    C. plain
    D. No change is necessary.

30. With Hobbes as his cohort, the destructive Calvin could <u>victimize</u> his babysitter, Rosalyn. He might lock her out
                                                        A

of the house or, <u>worse,</u> <u>calls</u> her boyfriend.
                    B   C

    A. victimized
    B. worst
    C. call
    D. No change is necessary.

31. When Hobbes was at his <u>side, the</u> insecure Calvin could ask unanswerable questions about the <u>universe or</u>
                                    A   B

express his fear that sometimes the world <u>was "a</u> pretty mean place."
                                              C

    A. side the
    B. universe, or
    C. was, "a
    D. No change is necessary.

32. Sometimes it was <u>mean, Moe, the school bully, extorted</u> quarters from Calvin or just beat him up for no reason, for instance.

    A. mean, Moe the school bully extorted
    B. mean. Moe, the school bully, extort
    C. mean. Moe, the school bully, extorted
    D. No change is necessary.

33. At least the end of Calvin and Hobbes <u>offer</u> <u>peace to</u> the child's beleaguered <u>mother and father</u> and to his
                                      A   B   C

teacher, Miss Wormwood.

    A. offers
    B. peace: to
    C. Mother and Father
    D. No change is necessary.

34. Faithful <u>readers, though,</u> would certainly be <u>pleased</u> to see more of the devilish <u>Calvin, and</u> not just on the rear
                   A   B   C

end of a truck!

    A. readers though,
    B. please
    C. Calvin. And
    D. No change is necessary.

Directions: Choose the underlined word or phrase that is unnecessary in the context of the passage.

35. *Night of the Living Dead* has gained a <u>wide</u> audience as one of the greatest <u>horror</u> films ever made, <u>largely</u> due to
                                       A   B   C

the special effects artist, <u>by the name of</u> Tom Savini, who created <u>incredibly believable</u> "living dead."
                                 D   E

    A. wide
    B. horror
    C. largely
    D. by the name of
    E. incredibly believable

36. Floyd, feared <u>initially</u> as the largest hurricane <u>of the century</u>, was the most costly <u>natural</u> disaster <u>in U.S. history</u>
                    A   B   C   D

because <u>of the fact that</u> it caused massive evacuations in Florida and extensive flooding from the Carolinas to
                  E

New England.

    A. initially
    B. of the century
    C. natural
    D. in U.S. history
    E. of the fact that

37. Deciding on a <u>college</u> major is a problem facing most freshmen. Counselors recommend that students narrow
                     A

<u>down</u> the possibilities by taking <u>vocational</u> preference tests and by <u>carefully</u> examining their <u>academic</u> strengths
 B   C   D   E

and weaknesses.

   A. college
   B. down
   C. vocational
   D. carefully
   E. academic

Directions: Choose the sentence that logically and correctly expresses the comparison.

38. A. It is as unlikely to snow in Miami as Key West.
   B. It is as unlikely to snow in Miami as it is in Key West.
   C. Snow in Miami is as scarce as Key West.

39. A. Hurricane Floyd caused more damage from flooding
   B. Hurricane Floyd caused more damage from flooding than from any factor.
   C. Hurricane Floyd caused more damage from flooding than from any other factor.

40. A. Developed in the 20th century, geodesic domes are said to be structurally stronger and more energy efficient.
   B. Geodesic domes, developed in the 20th century, are said to be structurally stronger as well as more energy efficient.
   C. Geodesic domes, developed in the 20th century, are said to be structurally stronger and more energy efficient than traditional buildings.

CLAST-Based Objective Test, Form B

Name_____   Date_____

1. _____   20. _____   39. _____

2. _____   21. _____   40. _____

3. _____   22. _____   Score _____

4. _____   23. _____

5. _____   24. _____

6. _____   25. _____

7. _____   26. _____

8. _____   27. _____

9. _____   28. _____

10. _____   29. _____

11. _____   30. _____

12. _____   31. _____

13. _____   32. _____

14. _____   33. _____

15. _____   34. _____

16. _____   35. _____

17. _____   36. _____

18. _____   37. _____

19. _____   38. _____

CLAST-Based Objective Test Answer Key and Correction Chart, Form B

Question	Answer	Hodges' Section	Writer's Section
1	B	6a	22e
2	C	3a	19a
3	D	12e	31e
4	B	2	18
5	C	28a	21e
6	D	13	31g
7	A	15a	33a
8	B	27a	N/A
9	C	18c	36c
10	D	4b	20b
11	D	18	36
12	A	25b	20f
13	B	26a	25a
14	A	26a	25a
15	B	26a	25a
16	C	25b	20f
17	C	25a	20e
18	A	20a	29a
19	A	20a	29a
20	C	20a	29a
21	C	24b	24b
22	D	24b	24b
23	D	24b	24b
24	A	4c	20c
25	A	28a	21e
26	C	17d	35d
27	C	12e	31e
28	C	5b	21b
29	B	18	36
30	C	7a	22a
31	D	12	31
32	C	3a	19a
33	A	7a	22a
34	D	12e	31e
35	D	21b	30b
36	E	21b	30b
37	B	21b	30b
38	B	22c	23h
39	B	22c	23h
40	C	22c	23h

CLAST-Based Essay Test, Form B

Directions for the Essay: You have an hour to compose an expository or a persuasive essay in response to **one** of the following topics:

Topic one: a little-known hero who should be more widely respected than he/she is

---

or

Topic two: a skill, a talent, or an attribute which students should acquire

---

After you have selected your topic, be sure that:

- you fully and logically address the topic,
- you support your ideas with concrete and convincing details,
- your approach remains coherent and unified,
- you choose appropriate and effective words, and
- you avoid errors of punctuation, capitalization, spelling, and/or syntax.

Remember to think and plan before you write and to save time to proofread. The reader (teacher or test scorer) will not penalize you for handwriting, but please write legibly to allow the evaluator(s) to judge the paper's content fairly. Add or neatly cross out information if necessary.

Use the following pages for your planning and final copy. Since any "brainstorming" or outlining that you do will not be used to score your paper, mark through such material so that the evaluator(s) may clearly see where your essay begins.

81

CLAST-Based Essay Test, Form B

Answer Sheet

Name_____

Date_____ /

_____

_____

_____

_____

_____

_____

_____

_____

_____

_____

_____

_____

_____

_____

_____

_____

_____

_____

_____

_____

_____

_____

_____

TASP-BASED TESTS

Description of Tests

This test contains two components: a precourse component (Form A) and a postcourse component (Form B). Each component consists of an essay assignment and objective questions, both of which test students' skills in composition, sentence structure, usage, and grammar. Each objective test is followed by a test answer key and correction chart, as well as a handbook chart describing the errors and showing the relevant chapter and section in *The Hodges' Harbrace Handbook*. Included with the tests are suggestions for general testing procedures and for administering the essay and the objective tests. Also included are suggestions for testing materials, time limits, and methods for scoring and interpreting results.

Suggestions for General Testing Procedures

1. To facilitate handling of the completed examinations, the examiner may wish to provide paper of uniform size.

2. Because students may arrive at the testing location without watches, they may benefit from having a large clock in a highly visible location in the testing location. Another option is to write the time on a chalkboard at regular intervals during the examination.

3. To reduce student anxiety, the examiner may wish to explain that these tests will not disqualify them from attendance at the institution, and that the scores will be used only to place students in the appropriate levels of composition courses.

Suggestions for Administering the Essay Test

Necessary materials: Timer, pens or pencils for students, notebooks or other lined paper.

Time limits: The essay test is designed to fit into the standard 50-minute class period, but timing is not essential to test validity.

Scoring and interpreting the results: Essays should be scored according to the TASP standards as described in *The Official TASP® Test Study Guide*.

Suggestions for Administering the Objective Test

Necessary materials: Timer, pens or pencils for students, answer sheets (which may be reproduced from the master answer sheets in this booklet or which may be computer cards, Scantron sheets, or notebook paper with answers numbered 1–50).

Time limits: The tests are designed to fit into the standard 50-minute class period, but timing is not essential to test validity.

Scoring and interpreting the results: Grade students according to the number of correct answers. Because students are not penalized for wrong answers, encourage them to make an effort to answer as many questions as possible in the examination. If the test results will determine passing or failing, this grading scale may be helpful:

90 to 100% = A
80 to 89% = B
70 to 79% = C
60 to 69% = D
00 to 59% = F

TASP-Based Objective Writing Test, Form A

This test contains items for the objective writing test. Your score will be based on the number of correct answers. There is no penalty for wrong answers, so it is to your advantage to answer every question. Please do not write in the test book. Answer marks should be neat and clear. If you make a mistake or want to change an answer, erase your first answer completely. There is only one correct answer for each item. You will have 50 minutes to complete the writing test. There are 50 items.

Directions: Read the following passages. Then choose the best answer for each question.

[1]Despite the love of flowers that was so prevalent in the nineteenth century, many people held the notion that having plants inside the house was unhealthy. [2]Their were even superstitious people who ascribed vampire characteristics to certain flowers, especially if grown in sleeping rooms. [3]Although such notions were thoroughly debunked by turn-of-the-century horticultural experts and household gardeners. [4]A vocal minority held fast to their vampire theories well into the twentieth century.

[5]The only truly troublesome aspect of window gardening was the insects: aphids, red spider mites, and mealy bugs. [6]The latter two were removed by hand and the leaves sprayed with plain water from a syringe. [7]When the water dried, the plant might be dusted with plain red-pepper powder. [8]Aphids were often destroyed with tobacco. [9]Most effective was plain, dried chewing tobacco, either ground in a mortar and applied as dust, or boiled in water, cooled, and used as a spray. [10]Some gardeners burned the tobacco, incense style, which might be fine in a greenhouse but in the parlor would tend to drive away occupants and aphids alike.

1.   Which sentence contains an error in sentence structure?

   A.   Sentence 3
   B.   Sentence 5
   C.   Sentence 9
   D.   Sentence 10

2.   Which sentence contains an error in usage?

   A.   Sentence 2
   B.   Sentence 4
   C.   Sentence 7
   D.   Sentence 10

3.   Which of the following is an adjective?

   A.   Sentence 1: love
   B.   Sentence 5: aspect
   C.   Sentence 6: syringe
   D.   Sentence 7: plain

[1]One of the most important American women painters is Mary Cassatt (1844–1926). [2]She was born to a prominent Pittsburgh, Pennsylvania family, and as child, she traveled across Europe with her parents and siblings. [3]When they returned to America, she followed her interest in painting, entering the Pennsylvania Academy of Fine Art in Philadelphia when she was eighteen. [4]By 1864 she was ready to study abroad. [5]She returned too Paris to study the old master paintings at the Louvre and in other European museums in Italy, Spain, and Belgium. [6]——— she had studied with academic painters, she was ready to follow her independent ideas.

[7]By 1874 she had settled in Paris where she would live for the rest of her life. [8]Here she found other painters who liked some of her ideas about art. [9]She resisted a photographic representation of her subjects and instead presented her impressions of her subject matter. [10]She was especially interested in asymmetrical compositions and in presenting her subjects in natural and informal positions. [11]As her style matured, her paintings were noticed by the French painter Edgar Degas. [12]He encouraged her work and invited her to exhibit her paintings with other artists who came to be known as the impressionist group.

[13]Cassatt's paintings are still admired today. [14]Although she never married or had children, many of the portraits examine the relationship of a mother and her child. [15]Her work is never overly sentimental, but her expression of the love and tenderness of a mother for her child is very appealing. [16]Interestingly, Cassatt never used paid models, preferring to use her family and friends in her paintings.

[17]By 1914 Cassatt's sight began to fail her, and although she continued to live in Paris, she stopped painting. [18]One of her last contributions to the art of the impressionists was her encouragement of their work to wealthy Americans. [19]She certainly important in forming some of the best collections of impressionistic art in America.

4. Which underlined word or words should be replaced by a more specific term?

   A. Sentence 2: prominent
   B. Sentence 6: independent
   C. Sentence 8: liked
   D. Sentence 10: asymmetrical

5. Which sentence contains an error in sentence structure?

   A. Sentence 3
   B. Sentence 4
   C. Sentence 9
   D. Sentence 19

6. What word or phrase inserted in the blank in sentence 6 would help the reader understand that logical sequence in this passage?

   A. However
   B. Although
   C. For example
   D. When

7. Information in sentences 1, 6, 13, and 15 contributes primarily to which of the following?

   A. Paragraph development
   B. Paragraph coherence
   C. Paragraph transition
   D. Main idea of the paragraph

8. Which sentence contains an error in usage?

   A. Sentence 5
   B. Sentence 8
   C. Sentence 12
   D. Sentence 14

9. Which word or phrase if substituted for the word "wealthy" in sentence 18 has a more negative connotation?

   A. Filthy rich
   B. Prominent
   C. Well off
   D. Upper class

[1]Sir Isaac Newton formulated a principle stating that everything in the physical universe exerts a force on everything else. [2]That means that each object in the universe pulls on the earth. [3]Of course, the closest celestial objects, the sun and the moon, exert the greatest force. [4]Their combined forces create earth's ocean and land tides.

[5]Ocean tides dramatically reveal the effects of the sun and the moon on the planet. [6]Twice a day, earth's vast oceans rise in accordance with the moon's gravitational pull. [7]Land tides are less visible than ocean tides but do

occur nonetheless. [8]As the moon passes overhead, the earth bulging like a big old fat pumpkin in November, causing the water to rise. [9]The highest tides, or "spring tides," appear during the full and new moon's when the moon is aligned with the sun, adding an extra one third of the moon's force. [10]"Neap tides," the lowest each month, occur when the sun and moon are out of alignment during the quarter phase. [11]When the moon is directly overhead, the surface of the earth raises as much as three inches. [12]However, the entire process of lifting and settling takes twelve hours, and most people remain oblivious to the phenomena.

10. What sentence has an error in punctuation?

    A. Sentence 4
    B. Sentence 6
    C. Sentence 9
    D. Sentence 10

11. Which sentence contains an error in usage?

    A. Sentence 4
    B. Sentence 6
    C. Sentence 7
    D. Sentence 11

12. Because of its position in the paragraph, which sentence disrupts the writer's logical sequence of development?

    A. Sentence 2
    B. Sentence 3
    C. Sentence 5
    D. Sentence 7

13. Where should the sentence be moved to maintain the logical sequence of ideas?

    A. Sentence 5
    B Sentence 8
    C. Sentence 10
    D. Sentence 11

14. Which change should be made in the passage?

    A. Sentence 8: Change "bulging" to "bulges"
    B. Sentence 9: Eliminate the comma after "spring tides"
    C. Sentence 11: Add "and" after "overhead"
    D. Sentence 12: Eliminate the comma after "hours"

15. Which sentence contains a level of diction that is inconsistent with the level of the rest of the passage?

    A. Sentence 1
    B. Sentence 3
    C. Sentence 8
    D. Sentence 10

[1]Like so many baby mammals, young elephants spend a great deal of their time playing. [2]They engage in butting matches; they chase one another around the great moving pillars of adult elephants' legs; they wallow ecstatically in mud. [3]Watch them doing so and you can have no doubt that they are enjoying themselves hugely, just as human children do in a playground. [4]Play, _____, also has a serious and valuable purpose. [5]It is a way of learning. [6]One of the first things an elephant has to discover is how to use its trunk. [7]When an elephant is only a month or two old, the long dangling object in front of its face is obviously a puzzle to it. [8]The young elephant will shake its head

and observe how this curious appendage flops about sometimes it trips up over the trunk. [9]Also, when the young elephant goes down to a waterhole to drink, it crouches down and awkwardly sips from its mouth. [10]Not until it is four or five months old does it discover the remarkable fact that water can be sniffed up into the trunk, and then, if the elephant blows out, it can hose the water into its mouth that discovery of course leads to a whole new set of possibilities for games.

16. What is the writer's primary purpose of this passage?

    A. To demonstrate the similarities between baby elephants and children
    B. To entertain the audience
    C. To inform the audience that elephants, when young, are often awkward and clumsy
    D. To explain the dual functions that playing serves in the baby elephant's development

17. Which sentence needs to be revised to eliminate wordiness?

    A. Sentence 2
    B. Sentence 3
    C. Sentence 7
    D. Sentence 10

18. Which sentence contains an error in sentence structure?

    A. Sentence 2
    B. Sentence 5
    C. Sentence 8
    D. None of the above

19. Which words or phrases, when inserted in the blank in Sentence 4, would help the reader understand the relationship between the ideas in the passage?

    A. therefore
    B. first
    C. in sum
    D. however

20. Which change is needed in the passage?

    A. Sentence 1: Eliminate the comma after "mammals."
    B. Sentence 2: Change the semicolons after "matches" and "legs" to commas.
    C. Sentence 8: Insert a comma after "head."
    D. Sentence 10: Insert commas after "discovery" and "course."

[1]In America today most people do not like to think about death. [2]Because of our aversion to death and all things associated with it, we are often unprepared to deal with the practical matters that are associated with dying. [3]Unfortunately, the funeral home industry is counting on our distracted grief when we are making our final arrangements. [4]How many people have selected their caskets, purchased their lots in a cemetery, or planned for the "final" expenses? [5]Most people under the age of 65 have not.

[6]The cost of a simple burial continues to escalate, and even being cremated is not inexpensive. [7]At a time of great sorrow, families are asked to consider what the "dearly departed" would have wanted in a casket. [8]The choices from fine woods and precious metals. [9]An important consideration seems to be weather the casket is water-tight or not. [10]A simple pine box is not always available.

[11]_____, the survivors must pay for the opening and closing of the grave, a headstone or marker, and other costs that are not always obvious (e.g., embalming). [12]Should we save up for our burial costs? [13]Probably everybody should make some final plans about these final moments. [14]Unfortunately, most of us do not want to think about our deaths; however some planning might help our loved ones during a difficult time.

21. What word if inserted in the blank of sentence 11 would help the reader to connect the paragraph with the one that comes before it?

    A. On the other hand
    B. Finally
    C. Furthermore
    D. First

22. Which change needs to be made in the passage?

    A. Sentence 2: Change "we" to "you"
    B. Sentence 4: Change "have" to "has"
    C. Sentence 7: Change the period to a question mark
    D. Sentence 9: Change "weather" to "whether"

23. What method of development has the writer chosen for this passage?

    A. Definition
    B. Classification
    C. Persuasion
    D. Narration

24. Which sentence contains an error in sentence structure?

    A. Sentence 5
    B. Sentence 6
    C. Sentence 7
    D. Sentence 8

25. Which sentence contains an error in punctuation?

    A. Sentence 6
    B. Sentence 11
    C. Sentence 12
    D. Sentence 14

26. Which of the following is an adjective?

    A. Sentence 4: people
    B. Sentence 8: final
    C. Sentence 11: survivors
    D. Sentence 12: up

[1]How I enjoyed watching my mother make a quilt. [2]First, she pieced together the top. [3]Would this color look best against this one or another? [4]Next, she prepared the lining. [5]Sometimes, for the lining, she managed to buy a soft, warm piece of flannel. [6]Then, she would search out and putting together her homemade quilting frame. [7]Occasionally, she propped the frame on chairs, but more often, it was suspended on wires or stout cords from the ceiling, so that she could lower or raise it, as needed. [8]Some frames had small nails across which the lining was stretched, but I remember that my mother whipstitched hers to the frame. [9]Next, came a layer of fluffy white cotton—often grown on our farm—that she used for batting. [10]Its cottony smell filled the air. [11]Last of all came the colorful quilt top, which she basted all around the lining. [12]Once finished, she marked a quilting pattern using chalk attached to a string. [13]Sometimes she used a shell pattern; at other times, she quilted in squares. [14]How deftly her hand applied the needle. [15]Sometimes she let me try my hand, but I think she took out my long stitches when I wasn't looking.

27. Which sentence contains an error in punctuation?

    A. Sentence 4
    B. Sentence 8
    C. Sentence 9
    D. Sentence 13

28. Which change should be made to eliminate an error in parallel structure?

    A. Sentence 5: Change "managed" to "manage"
    B. Sentence 6: Change "putting" to "put"
    C. Sentence 8: Change "across which" to "in which"
    D. Sentence 11: Change "came" to "comes"

29. What method of structuring paragraphs has the writer used in this passage?

    A. General to particular
    B. Particular to general
    C. Spatial order
    D. Chronological order

[1]Most good students do not come into this world with good study habits. [2]Unfortunately, good habits have to be learned and practiced before they become the routine way of studying. [3]Most teachers recommended that students prepare for class by studying for three hours for every one hour in class. [4]What in the world would you do for three hours? [5]That study time must be carefully planned and time set aside for test preparation and when you have to write an essay. [6]If students would practice good study habits, they would find that assignments and tests would not be as difficult.

30. In which sentence does the tone seem out of place in this paragraph?

    A. Sentence 2
    B. Sentence 3
    C. Sentence 4
    D. Sentence 5

31. Which sentence needs to be revised for parallel structure?

    A. Sentence 1
    B. Sentence 2
    C. Sentence 3
    D. Sentence 5

32. Which sentence contains a distracting shift in tense?

    A. Sentence 1
    B. Sentence 2
    C. Sentence 3
    D. Sentence 6

33. What is the writer's primary purpose in this passage?

    A. To complain about student preparation
    B. To help students think about their study habits
    C. To make excuses for students' habits
    D. To imply that good students are born that way

[1]With a little practice and experimentation, I learned the basics of great grilling. [2]The most important step is preparing the grill so that meatless menus don't come out charred on the outside and raw on the inside. [3]I prefer gas grills because it takes about five minutes to heat and doesn't require any special preparation. [4]If you want to use a charcoal grill, it's best to line the bowl with foil to reflect heat (which decreases cooking time) and to make cleanup easy. [5]You can use either a gas or a charcoal grill. [6]I like lump charcoal made from hardwood (such as apple, oak, and mesquite), which impart a nice smoky flavor to food. [7]After lighting, regular charcoal requires 20–30 minutes to heat before you can begin grilling. [8]Next, to prevent your vegetables from falling into the flames, use a grilling rack, a baking sheet with holes in it. [9]This rack can sit over either a charcoal or a gas grill and is available at gourmet cookware stores. [10]Skewering your vegetables is another way to keep them out of the fire. [11]Even when the weather is cold and rainy you can still grill up a feast indoors with a stovetop grill. [12]Available for less than $20 at discount and cookware stores, stovetop grills work by steam heat. [13]The grill goes directly over a burner, and water steams from an undergrill rim. [14]Using a medium flame, heat the grill until splashed-on drops of water jump. [15]Then you're ready to start cooking.

34. This passage was primarily written for which audience?

    A. Experienced chefs
    B. Vegetarian cooks
    C. Campers
    D. Outdoor caterers

35. Because of its position in the passage, which part interrupts the logical sequence of development?

    A. Sentence 3
    B. Sentence 5
    C. Sentence 9
    D. Sentence 12

36. Where should the aforementioned part be moved to preserve the logical sequence of development?

    A. After Sentence 2
    B. After Sentence 6
    C. After Sentence 10
    D. After Sentence 14

37. Which correction in punctuation should be made?

    A. Sentence 1: Delete the comma after "experimentation"
    B. Sentence 4: Change "it's" to "its"
    C. Sentence 11: Insert a comma after "rainy"
    D. Sentence 12: Eliminate the comma after "stores," and insert a semicolon

38. Which change should be made in the passage?

    A. Sentence 3: Change "don't" to "do not"
    B. Sentence 4: Change "to make" to "making"
    C. Sentence 6: Change "impart" to "imparts"
    D. Sentence 15: Change "you're" to "your"

39. What changes should be made?

    A. Sentence 1: Change "learned" to "learn"
    B. Sentence 3: Change "it" to "they," "takes" to "take," and "doesn't" to "don't"
    C. Sentence 8: Change "Next" to "Consequently"
    D. Sentence 10: Change "is" to "are"

[1]The wedding—a ceremony binding two people together, presumably forever—is supposed to be an unforgettable experience. [2]Joan Didion, in "Marrying Absurd," and Andrea Lee, in the "The Wedding," examine this much-revered tradition. [3]Although the ceremonies discussed in the two essays take place within different cultures (Las Vegas and the Soviet Union, respectively), both show the reader how the wedding may be cheapened and transformed into a practical business. [4]Didion and Lee accomplish this by scrutinizing the marriage "business," using extended metaphors of "industry" and the "factory" throughout their works. [5]"Industry" is a fitting term used by Didion to depict Las Vegas marriages; and while the same word seems equally admirable in illustrating Lees view of the Soviet nuptials, she prefers the term "factory." [6]The distinction between the two may be made if one considers the differences in the two cultures. [7]American "industry" is big business; it is capitalism. [8]It manufactures goods or offers services, but its primary concern is to make the public want them. [9]The Soviet "factory" is government run and, according to communist doctrine, uniformity is all important. [10]This principle applies not only to the products, but also to the factories themselves. [11]The "wedding industry" in Las Vegas is the epitome of American free enterprise: Didion calls the field "intensely competitive," and advertising is widespread and aggressive, enumerating all available options. [12]At the Palace of Weddings in Moscow; however, the ceremony is performed in the socialist spirit of mass production, and Lee says that after the wedding she felt "as if [she'd] just finished touring a factory." [13]Whether weddings are accomplished through capitalism or communism, competition or institutionalization, "wedding industry" or "marriage factory," the resulting attitudes and atmospheres are similar.

40. Which sentence contains an error in sentence structure?

    A. Sentence 3
    B. Sentence 7
    C. Sentence 11
    D. Sentence 12

41. Which underlined word should be replaced by a more specific and accurate term?

    A. Sentence 4: scrutinizing
    B. Sentence 5: admirable
    C. Sentence 9: uniformity
    D. Sentence 11: aggressive

42. What changes need to be made in the passage?

    A. Sentence 3: Change "(Las Vegas and the Soviet Union, respectively)," to "(Las Vegas and the Soviet Union respectively)."
    B. Sentence 5: Change "Lees" to "Lee's."
    C. Sentence 11: Delete the colon after "free enterprise," and insert a comma.
    D. None of the above

43. What is the writer's primary purpose in this passage?

    A. To convince the audience to take marriage more seriously
    B. To explain the differences between the United States and the Soviet Union
    C. To analyze the metaphors that the two writers use to describe wedding ceremonies in the Soviet Union and the United States
    D. None of the above

[1]People have learned how to manipulate the English language in many ways in order to achieve a goal or purpose. [2]Car salesmen, for instance, may tell prospective buyers that a car has a "lifetime warranty," which sounds good but may really mean only that the company will replace a defective mirror, but the buyer will have to pay if the carburetor falls out. [3]They just want to sell their quota of cars. [4]People use these clouded phrases, called "euphemisms," for every situation from cars to death and war because they want to hide truths they feel are too hideous to reveal or because other words and phrases might hinder their purpose. [5]In short, using euphemisms to conceal situations that might hurt us if expressed in clearer, more concise terms. [6]A prime example of euphemism be the home-improvement specialist's phrase for "burglar alarm"—"security systems." [7]While the phrase "burglar

alarm" conjures up images in the consumers' minds of thieves lurking in the dark, ready to break into <u>their</u> homes, the term "security system" or "home-safety system" conjures up few negative images at all. [8]Instead, the words reinforce the idea that through high-tech advancement, the consumer can be protected and secure, invulnerable to criminal activity. [9]Ultimately, the euphemism serves two functions: They alleviate the home owner's fear of being violated, or worse, actually confronting an intruder, and it boosts the salespeople's chance at making a sale by allowing them to dance around the frightening idea that the device they are selling is intended to prevent.

44. Which change needs to be made?

    A. Sentence 2: Change "salesmen" to "salespeople."
    B. Sentence 3: Change "their" to "his."
    C. Sentence 5: Change "using" to "to use."
    D. Sentence 8: Change "high-tech" to "hightech"

45. Which sentence contains an underlined pronoun that is unclear because it is too far from its antecedent?

    A. Sentence 3
    B. Sentence 4
    C. Sentence 7
    D. All of the above

46. Which sentence should be revised to eliminate wordiness?

    A. Sentence 2
    B. Sentence 3
    C. Sentence 6
    D. Sentence 8

47. Which changes need to be made?

    A. Sentence 1: Change "have learned" to "learn."
    B. Sentence 6: Change "specialist's" to "specialists."
    C. Sentence 9: Change "they alleviate" to "it alleviates."
    D. None of the above

48. Which sentence contains an error in sentence structure?

    A. Sentence 3
    B. Sentence 5
    C. Sentence 7
    D. Sentence 8

49. Which of the following words is an adverb?

    A. prospective
    B. quota
    C. hideous
    D. really

50. Which change needs to be made?

    A. Sentence 2: Change "a car has" to "a car have."
    B. Sentence 6: Change "be" to "is."
    C. Sentence 8: Change "reinforce" to "reinforces."
    D. None of the above

TASP-Based Objective Writing Test, Form A

Answer Sheet

Name_____

Date_____

1. _____
2. _____
3. _____
4. _____
5. _____
6. _____
7. _____
8. _____
9. _____
10. _____
11. _____
12. _____
13. _____
14. _____
15. _____
16. _____
17. _____
18. _____
19. _____

20. _____
21. _____
22. _____
23. _____
24. _____
25. _____
26. _____
27. _____
28. _____
29. _____
30. _____
31. _____
32. _____
33. _____
34. _____
35. _____
36. _____
37. _____
38. _____

39. _____
40. _____
41. _____
42. _____
43. _____
44. _____
45. _____
46. _____
47. _____
48. _____
49. _____
50. _____

Score _____

TASP-Based Objective Test Answer Key and Correction Chart, Form A

Question	Answer	*Hodges'* Section	*Writer's* Section
1	A	2	18
2	A	18c	36c
3	D	4b	20b
4	C	20a	29a
5	D	2	18
6	B	31b	3c
7	A	31c	2d
8	A	18c	36c
9	A	20a	29a
10	C	15a	33a
11	D	7a	22a
12	D	31a	3c
13	C	31b	3c
14	A	2	18
15	C	19c	28c
16	D	32a	1e
17	D	21b	30b
18	C	3a	19a
19	D	31b	3c
20	D	12e	31e
21	C	31b	3c
22	D	18c	36c
23	C	32a	1e
24	D	2	18
25	D	12b	31b
26	B	4b	20b
27	C	13	31g
28	B	26a	25a
29	D	31c	2d
30	C	31a	3c
31	D	26a	25a
32	C	27a	N/A
33	B	32a	1e
34	B	32a	1e
35	B	31a	3c
36	A	31b	3c
37	C	12b	31b
38	C	6a	22e
39	B	6b	21d
40	D	14c	32c
41	B	20a	29a
42	B	15a	33a
43	C	32a	1e
44	A	19d	28d
45	A	28a	21e
46	A	21b	30b
47	C	6b	21d
48	B	2	18
49	D	4	20
50	B	7a	22a

TASP-Based Essay Test, Form A₁

Essay Directions: Your assignment is to write a multiple-paragraph essay of 300–600 words, in response to the following question. You have a minimum of 50 minutes to complete this essay; during that time, you should plan, write, and edit the essay. Do not write a rough draft and recopy.

Grading Criteria

Your essay will be scored holistically on how well it states a whole message to a specific audience for the given purpose. Your essay will be graded on the following criteria:

Appropriateness:	Answering the specific question and using appropriate language for the writing situation
Unity and focus:	Maintaining your main idea within the essay and within individual paragraphs
Development:	Including examples that prove your position
Organization:	Sequencing your ideas logically and clearly
Sentence structure:	Writing complete and correct sentences
Usage:	Using standard grammar and word choices
Mechanics:	Using standard capitalization, spelling, and punctuation

Writing Assignment

Should teenaged drivers be restricted in their driving privileges? Proponents of this plan would restrict teenaged drivers to driving during the daytime and only with a licensed driver over the age of twenty-one. They see this measure as a way to save lives. Opponents of this plan want teenagers to be able to drive themselves to school and other activities. They don't want all teenagers punished because a few teenagers don't drive responsibly.

TASP-Based Essay Test, Form A₂

Essay Directions: Your assignment is to write a multiple-paragraph essay of 300–600 words, in response to the following question. You have a minimum of 50 minutes to complete this essay; during that time, you should plan, write, and edit the essay. Do not write a rough draft and recopy.

Grading Criteria

Your essay will be scored holistically on how well it states a whole message to a specific audience for the given purpose. Your essay will be graded on the following criteria:

Appropriateness: Answering the specific question and using appropriate language for the writing situation
Unity and focus: Maintaining your main idea within the essay and within individual paragraphs
Development: Including examples that prove your position
Organization: Sequencing your ideas logically and clearly
Sentence structure: Writing complete and correct sentences
Usage: Using standard grammar and word choices
Mechanics: Using standard capitalization, spelling, and punctuation

Writing Assignment

Should grandparents have the legal right to visitation with their grandchildren? Proponents say that grandparents have a special relationship that must be protected by law. Opponents say that the biological parents, barring any proven child abuse, should decide if the grandparents or anyone else should have a relationship with their children.

TASP-Based Essay Test, Form A₃

Essay Directions: Your assignment is to write a multiple-paragraph essay of 300–600 words, in response to the following question. You have a minimum of 50 minutes to complete this essay; during that time, you should plan, write, and edit the essay. Do not write a rough draft and recopy.

Grading Criteria

Your essay will be scored holistically on how well it states a whole message to a specific audience for the given purpose. Your essay will be graded on the following criteria:

Appropriateness: Answering the specific question and using appropriate language for the writing situation
Unity and focus: Maintaining your main idea within the essay and within individual paragraphs
Development: Including examples that prove your position
Organization: Sequencing your ideas logically and clearly
Sentence structure: Writing complete and correct sentences
Usage: Using standard grammar and word choices
Mechanics: Using standard capitalization, spelling, and punctuation

Writing Assignment

Should your city pass an ordinance requiring bicycle riders to wear helmets? Proponents believe that wearing helmets prevents injuries and saves lives. Opponents do not want an ordinance requiring helmets because they do not want their freedom of choice taken away.

Name_____   Date_____

_____

_____

_____

_____

_____

_____

_____

_____

_____

_____

_____

_____

_____

_____

_____

_____

_____

_____

_____

_____

_____

_____

TASP-Based Objective Writing Test, Form B

This test contains items for the objective writing test. Your score will be based on the number of correct answers. There is no penalty for wrong answers, so it is to your advantage to answer every question. Please do not write in the test book. Answer marks should be neat and clear. If you make a mistake or want to change an answer, erase your first answer completely. There is only one correct answer for each item. You will have 50 minutes to complete the writing test. There are 50 items.

Directions: Read the following passages. Then choose the best answer for each question.

[1]During the Industrial Revolution in England, workers who were unemployed because of the advances of technology, <u>resorted</u> to violence to protest there condition. [2]They deliberately broke equipment that was important to the textile industries of lace and hosiery. [3]The movement began in 1811 in Nottingham, where the former employees broke knitting frames. [4]In a few years, similar events in Yorkshire and Lancashire in the cotton and wool mills. [5]The British government, fully supporting the new industrialists, <u>sent</u> thousands of troops to the area to maintain the peace. [6]Over 14,000 soldiers helped to stop the uprisings from 1811 to 1812. [7]The Luddites, as they came to be known, were severely punished. [8]In January of 1813 at York, fourteen Luddites were hanged.

[9]Obviously, the Luddites were not <u>successful</u> in stopping the Industrial Revolution, however, they are remembered today for their dramatic, yet honorable, resistance to what they saw as an end to their way of life. [10]Their primary success in the nineteenth century was to bring the question of the machine to the public. [11]Even today those who question the uncontrolled growth of technology use their name. [12]Today Luddites ask what is the <u>price</u> of technology and who is going to have to pay as the world relies more and more on better and faster technology?

1. What change needs to be made in the passage?

   A. Sentence 10: Change "their" to "its"
   B. Sentence 1: Remove the comma after "technology"
   C. Sentence 5: Capitalize "government"
   D. Sentence 11: Change "use" to "uses"

2. Which sentence contains an error in sentence structure?

   A. Sentence 4
   B. Sentence 12
   C. Sentence 8
   D. Sentence 6

3. Which sentence contains an error in punctuation?

   A. Sentence 3
   B. Sentence 7
   C. Sentence 8
   D. Sentence 9

4. In the sentence choices below, which underlined word needs to be replaced with a more specific term?

   A. Sentence 1: sank
   B. Sentence 5: dispatched
   C. Sentence 9: lucky
   D. Sentence 12: amount

5. Which sentence contains an error in usage?

    A. Sentence 7
    B. Sentence 1
    C. Sentence 5
    D. Sentence 8

[1]Eye contact is one of the most direct and powerful forms of nonverbal communication, allowing individuals to express a variety of emotions. [2]_____ a man's eyes might reveal that he is sad if he stares vacantly into space, gazes "emptily" at others, or cries. [3]_____, love can be communicated through the eyes. [4]A couple in love will often stare closely and fully into each other's eyes with minimal blinking. [5]This stare gives the couple a feeling of closeness and warmth. [6]Eye contact is also used to gain attention or to prevent another from loosing interest. [7]When speakers address a group, for example, they will shift their gaze across various members of the crowd throughout their speech. [8]This eye contact allows them to gain the individual attention of each member of the group, thus preventing anyone from feeling isolated or left out of the discussion. [9]Staring can also be used to gain the individual attention of a single person. [10]This form of visual attention is often used in crowded places where it might be inappropriate to shout at people to gain their attention.

[11]Facial expressions are also important clues to a person's feelings or mood. [12]Happiness, anger, and fear can all be detected through various expressions smiles are an indication of pleasure and happiness. [13]While people who smile communicate cheerfulness, a person gritting their teeth and squinting their eyebrows may be expressing anger. [14]When people are angry, their facial muscles are often tense and puckered. [15]This gesture tells others that something is wrong or that someone has made them angry, whether the people displaying the attitude will admit to being angry or not. [16]Fear, on the other hand, can be noticed when people's eyes widen and their mouths drop open. [17]Detecting these different expressions can help prepare people to interact successfully with others.

6. Which sentence contains an error in usage?

    A. Sentence 2
    B. Sentence 6
    C. Sentence 11
    D. None of the above

7. Which change should be made in the passage?

    A. Sentence 2: Change "a man's" to "a person's" and "he" to "she or he"
    B. Sentence 4: Change "each other's" to "their"
    C. Sentence 10: Change "their" to "his or her"
    D. Sentence 15: Change "others" to "other people"

8. Which sentence contains an error in sentence structure?

    A. Sentence 8
    B. Sentence 12
    C. Sentence 14
    D. Sentence 16

9. Which change should be made in the passage?

    A. Sentence 4: Change "with minimal blinking" to "with a minimal amount of blinking"
    B. Sentence 8: Change "allows" to "allowing"
    C. Sentence 13: Change "a person" to "those"
    D. Sentence 16: Change "noticed" to "notice"

10. Which words or phrases, if placed in the blanks in sentences 2 and 3, would effectively link the ideas in these sentences?

    A. For example; In conclusion
    B. Therefore; Likewise
    C. For instance; Likewise
    D. Certainly; Specifically

11. What is the writer's primary purpose in this passage?

    A. To convince the readers to be more aware of what they are communicating nonverbally
    B. To point out common examples of nonverbal communication and explain their possible meaning
    C. To explain to public speakers how they can become more effective lecturers
    D. To persuade the members of the audience to improve their relationships by studying nonverbal communication

12. The topic sentence or controlling idea can be found in which sentence?

    A. Sentence 1
    B. Sentence 3
    C. Sentence 6
    D. Sentence 9

13. Which technique of structuring and developing paragraphs has the writer relied on almost exclusively?

    A. Definition
    B. Classification
    C. Narration
    D. Enumeration

[1]Tropical vegetables use to be available only in areas that had large Hispanic populations. [2]Today, thanks to the increased popularity of Mexican cuisine and Mexican restaurants, tropical vegetables are starting to appear, although in limited supply, in the larger supermarkets in areas with minimal Latin American populations.

[3]Words such as *taco, tortilla, tamale, enchilada, chile con carne, guacamole,* and *gazpacho* have entered our vocabulary; it is only a matter of time before the names of the tropical vegetables enjoyed by Latin Americans will also have common usage. [4]Words such as *calabaza, jicama, nopales, plantain, yammi, yautia,* and *yucca* often appearing in recipes in magazines and newspapers. [5]Just as avocados, mangoes, kiwis, and papayas were sold only as interesting whatnots years ago and today are available in ample supply in most food markets, tropical vegetables may soon enjoy the same consumer acceptance.

14. Which sentence contains an error in sentence structure?

    A. Sentence 2
    B. Sentence 3
    C. Sentence 4
    D. Sentence 5

15. Which sentence contains a level of diction inconsistent with the diction in the other parts of the passage?

    A. Sentence 1
    B. Sentence 3
    C. Sentence 5
    D. None of the above

16. Which sentence contains an error in usage?

    A. Sentence 1
    B. Sentence 2
    C. Sentence 4
    D. Both B and C

[1]The ability for human beings to walk upright is an important evolutionary development. [2]Walking not only allows us to move about freely, but it can also be a form of recreation and exercise. [3]As an aerobic exercise, it provides many important benefits. [4]If a person can walk at a moderate pace for as much as 20 to 30 minutes per day, then they can achieve physical fitness. [5]Walking at that rate can strengthen bones and reduce the risk of heart disease, diabetes, and strokes. [6]This type of exercise can also have positive effects on psychological functions. [7]Some studies suggest that people who walk regularly at a fast rate might also improve their immune systems.

[8]Sometimes people walk to lose weight. [9]While increased activity, especially activity that is regular and rigorous, contributes to weight loss, it is necessary for those who seek a weight loss to reduce their daily caloric intake as well. [10]_____, walking for an hour a day may burn up only about 300 calories. [11]I certainly eat a lot more calories than that a day. [12]_____, people must reduce the number of calories as well as exercise in order to weigh less.

[13]_____, walking may have some benefits, which can't really be measured by science. [14]Those who walk regularly enjoy the outdoors: the beauty of a sunrise or sunset; the change in the seasons; the colors of the earth, and the animals that share this planet with us. [15]Sometimes those who walk will be refreshed by the change of scenery as they move about. [16]Some people talk about taking a walk to clear their minds. [17]Others walk to talk to each other.

[18]Walking at a moderate pace certainly has its benefits. [19]If people walk several times a week, they can help to reduce several potential health risks. [20]They can become more physically fit, and if they can reduce their calorie intake as they increase their walking, they can benefit from a weight loss. [21]As an aerobic exercise with many positive effects, walking is an exercise that should be encouraged.

17. Which transitions, if inserted in the blanks in sentences 10, 12, and 13, would provide for smooth connections for the reader?

    A. Therefore; On the other hand; Finally
    B. For example; Obviously; However
    C. On the other hand; For example; Therefore
    D. First; Secondly; Finally

18. Which sentence needs to be revised for parallel structure?

    A. Sentence 2
    B. Sentence 5
    C. Sentence 14
    D. None of the above

19. Which sentence contains an inappropriate shift?

    A. Sentence 6
    B. Sentence 11
    C. Sentence 18
    D. Sentence 21

20. Which sentence contains an error in usage?

    A. Sentence 4
    B. Sentence 10
    C. Sentence 17
    D. Sentence 19

[1]Humanity has three classes of living nonhuman enemies. [2]First, there are the great predators: lions, bears, sharks, and so on. [3]We treasure stories of Samson rending a lion, and we shudder over the movie *Jaws*. [4]Actually, however, those poor animals have been out-classed for thousands of years and could be driven to extinction with very little trouble if humanity really put its mind to it. [5]Second, there are the invisible parasites: the viruses, bacteria, protozoa, worms, and so on that in one way or another live at our expense and interfering with our health. [6]These are far more dangerous than the large predators, and we need only compare the Black Death of the fourteenth century with anything man-eating tigers could do. [7]In the past century and a quarter, however, we have learned ways of dealing with these disease producers, and the danger has vastly diminished. [8]That leaves the third group: unwanted plants, or weeds. [9]With very few exceptions, these are not apparently dangerous in themselves and are certainly not dramatic, for they do nothing but grow. [10]Yet in some ways, it is the most insidious and dangerous enemy of all.

21. What is the writer's primary purpose in the passage?

    A. To argue that wildlife conservation is important
    B. To explain the threat various plants and animals pose to humans
    C. To persuade the audience to take weeds more seriously
    D. None of the above

22. In which order has the writer arranged the details in the **paragraph**?

    A. Climactic order
    B. Spatial order
    C. Particular to general
    D. Chronological

23. Which change should be made?

    A. Sentence 3: Change "shudder" to "shuddered"
    B. Sentence 4: Change "its" to "it's"
    C. Sentence 8: Eliminate the colon after "group"
    D. Sentence 10: Change "it is" to "they are"

24. Which word is an adjective?

    A. Humanity
    B. shudder
    C. man-eating
    D. vastly

25. Which sentence needs to be revised for parallel structure?

    A. Sentence 2
    B. Sentence 5
    C. Sentence 7
    D. Sentence 9

[1]Cooking in a clay pot is a culinary technique that has been used by chefs since the time of the Roman Empire. [2]Food that is done like this is moist, flavorful, and low in fat. [3]It is a good idea to use fresh herbs when cooking in clay. [4]Since most dishes cook slowly, the seasonings thoroughly combines to make a delicious one-pot meal. [5]The chef must start this delightful dinner by soaking the clay pot in a sink full of clean, cool water. [6]This step is necessary because the water absorbed by the clay forms a tight seal that steams the food in the pot. [7]A complete dinner of chicken and things can be made in one pot, using very little fat. [8]Because the seal is important and necessary for proper cooking, the chef must not remove the top. [9]Therefore, there no basting or stirring. [10]Once the clay pot is in the oven, the cook is free to enjoy a good book or a long walk.

26. Which phrase doesn't fit the tone of the rest of the paragraph?

   A. Sentence 1: "a culinary technique"
   B. Sentence 2: "that is done like this"
   C. Sentence 6: "the water absorbed by the clay"
   D. Sentence 9: "no basting or stirring"

27. Which sentence contains an error in sentence structure?

   A. Sentence 3
   B. Sentence 4
   C. Sentence 5
   D. Sentence 9

28. Which change should be made to the passage?

   A. Sentence 2: Remove the comma after "moist"
   B. Sentence 3: Change "herbs" to "herb"
   C. Sentence 4: Change "combines" to "combine"
   D. Sentence 5: Remove the comma after "clean"

29. Which sentence seems out of place in the paragraph's sequence of ideas?

   A. Sentence 6
   B. Sentence 7
   C. Sentence 8
   D. Sentence 10

30. Where should the sentence be moved to maintain the logical sequence of ideas?

   A. After Sentence 2
   B. Before Sentence 6
   C. After Sentence 8
   D. After Sentence 10

31. Which underlined word should be replaced with a more specific term?

   A. Sentence 1: technique
   B. Sentence 4: thoroughly
   C. Sentence 6: absorbed
   D. Sentence 7: things

[1]As humans, our imagination provides us with the foundation we need to live a unique, meaningful, and independent existence. [2]Much as color or texture breathes life into a painting, our ability to imagine both shapes and gives dimension to our lives. [3]In fact, an existence without imagination renders us useless and vulnerable to those who do have the ability to imagine and who may decide to use this ability to control those who either don't have imagination or refuse to exercise it.

[4]Just for a moment, envision a society of beings without the capability of imagination the peoples professional choices in such a society are limited. [5]They cannot be scientists, for that would entail experimentation and hypothesis, characteristics of those with the imagination to question and conjecture. [6]They cannot be engineers because they do not possess the imagination to produce new designs. [7]The individuals could never become politicians because they would have to have the ability to compose new legislation, an activity requiring speculation about the causes of certain problems and the effects of the legislation designed to solve them. [8]There could never be any artists, playwrights, authors of fiction or nonfiction, musicians, fashion designers, architects, or inventors of any kind in this society because each of these positions require imagination. [9]In this hypocritical society, individuals can make no advancement; their existence is stagnant.

32. Which sentence contains an error in sentence structure?

    A. Sentence 2
    B. Sentence 4
    C. Sentence 7
    D. Sentence 8

33. Which change in punctuation should be made?

    A. Sentence 2: Delete the comma after "painting" and insert a semicolon
    B. Sentence 4: Change "peoples" to "people's"
    C. Sentence 5: Delete the comma after "hypothesis"
    D. Sentence 9: Delete the semicolon after "advancement" and insert a comma

34. Which change needs to be made?

    A. Sentence 2: Change "lives" to "lifes"
    B. Sentence 5: Change "scientists" to "a scientist"
    C. Sentence 6: Change "do not" to "does not"
    D. Sentence 8: Change "require" to "requires"

35. Which underlined word needs to be replaced by a more accurate term?

    A. Sentence 2: renders
    B. Sentence 5: entail
    C. Sentence 7: speculation
    D. Sentence 9: hypocritical

36. What technique has the writer used to structure and develop the passage?

    A. Comparison/contrast
    B. Cause/effect
    C. Definition
    D. Problem/solution

[1]The star nearest to us is Alpha Centauri. [2]It is only 4.3 light-years away. [3]That's not exactly next door, for that distance is equal to 25 trillion miles, which makes it a quarter of a million times as far away as our own Sun is. [4]Just the same, all other stars are further from us than Alpha Centauri is. [5]What's more, as best we can tell from this distance, Alpha Centauri is an almost identical twin to our Sun. [6]It is just about as large and as hot as our Sun and has very nearly the same chemical constitution. [7]The next nearest star that so closely resembles the Sun is about six times as far away as Alpha Centauri.

[8]It would seem, then, that if ever we try to explore some other star, the one we should surely aim for is Alpha Centauri. [9]Not only is it the closest star, but also, if it is so like our Sun, it may have planets very much like those of our solar system. [10]One perhaps that is rather Earth-like and that bears life. [11]There is a catch, however, and it may be an important one. [12]Alpha Centauri is not a single star, as our Sun is. [13]It is a "binary star," a system of two stars that swing about each other—a double star, so to speak. [14]The Alpha Centauri I've been speaking of as our Sun's twin is, actually, Alpha Centauri A, the brighter of the pair. [15]The other one, Alpha Centauri B, is smaller and more cooler and is only about a quarter as bright as Alpha Centauri A (or our Sun) is.

37. Which sentence contains an error in usage?

    A. Sentence 3
    B. Sentence 4
    C. Sentence 9
    D. Sentence 14

38. The passage was primarily written for which audience?

    A. Astronomers
    B. Persons interested in life on other planets
    C. Science-fiction fans
    D. Persons interested in stars

39. Which sentence contains an error in sentence structure?

    A. Sentence 4
    B. Sentence 6
    C. Sentence 10
    D. Sentence 15

40. Which change should be made?

    A. Sentence 3: Eliminate the comma after "miles," and insert a semicolon
    B. Sentence 5: Change "What's" to "Whats"
    C. Sentence 13: Change "swing" to "swings"
    D. Sentence 15: Change "more cooler" to "cooler"

41. Which technique has the writer used to fully develop each of the preceding paragraphs?

    A. Comparison/contrast
    B. Definition
    C. Narration
    D. Cause/effect

[1]In London near Saint Martin's Place at Trafalgar Square, there is a monument to a heroic nurse. [2]Many miles away in the snowy mountains of Alberta, Canada there is a national park named for this nurse who refused to neglect the sick and wounded even though it meant giving up her own life instead. [3]This nurse is Edith Cavell, who was born in Swardeston, England in December of 1865. [4]Even though she had to go through three years of training without the support of her family, she studied very hard. [5]She was so successful that she was selected to teach student nurses, and a doctor in Belgium, who was starting a nursing school, begged Nurse Cavell to teach in his school.

[6]In Belgium, Nurse Cavell found a real challenge as she trained young girls in basic nursing. [7]As if these difficulties were not enough, World War I soon broke out in Europe. [8]As Germany advanced on Belgium, Nurse Cavell and her staff treated all the wounded who came to their clinic. [9]They helped every soldier no matter if he were British, Belgium, French, or German. [10]In fact, two of the nurses at the clinic were German. [11]Eventual, Germany took over Belgium, and Nurse Cavell found herself under suspicion. [12]As a British citizen, she was considered to be an enemy to Germany.

[13]_____, Nurse Cavell had been helping the Allied soldiers to escape. [14]When the soldiers became strong enough to travel, she gave him food and clothing and helped them to escape to Holland. [15]On August 4, 1915, she was arrested by the Germans for being a spy and sentenced to execution. [16]Several countries around the world appealed to Germany to halt the execution. But Edith Cavell was shot by a firing squad on October 12, 1915. [17]The world was horrified to see this treatment of a woman who had helped others so courageously. [18]Her self-sacrifice and strength have been a source of inspiration for many people.

42. Which sentence should be changed?

    A. Sentence 2: Change "is" to "are"
    B. Sentence 4: Change "through" to "threw"
    C. Sentence 7: Change "As if" to "Like"
    D. Sentence 14: Change "gave him food" to "gave them food"

43. What method of organizing details has the writer followed in this passage?

   A. Spatial order
   B. Chronological order
   C. Climactic order
   D. General to specific order

44. What word or phrase, if inserted in the blank in sentence 13, would best serve as a transition between the paragraphs?

   A. Therefore
   B. As it turned out
   C. To the contrary
   D. Later that night

45. What is the writer's primary purpose in this passage?

   A. Edith Cavell was a very heroic nurse
   B. The Germans were cruel to invade Belgium
   C. Horrible events occur during wartime
   D. Nursing is a difficult and dangerous profession

46. Which change needs to be made?

   A. Sentence 2: Change "her" to "their"
   B. Sentence 5: Change "successful" to "successfully"
   C. Sentence 11: Change "Eventual" to "Eventually"
   D. Sentence 17: Change "had" to "has"

[1]Ben Balsley, an atmospheric scientist with the Cooperative Institute of Research in Environmental Science at the University of Colorado, has some advice for colleagues who want to find out more about climate patterns: Go fly a kite. [2]Picking up where Benjamin Franklin left off 240 years ago, Balsley hopes to usher in a new age of atmospheric kite research.

[3]One of the advantages of using kites is that they can remain in one spot in the atmosphere, there they gather information about temperature, water vapor, radiation, ozone levels, and so forth. "There's no other way of getting these data," Balsley says. [4]"Satellites can't provide detailed pictures, and planes can't sit in one spot."

[5]Stronger, lightweight materials—Kevlar lines and Mylar and carbon fibers for kite bodies—allows kites to fly higher and carry heavier instrument payloads than ever before. [6]In a 1990 experiment, Balsley and his kite-designing pals William Tyrrell and Joe Williams lofted two kites more than two miles above Christmas Island in the Pacific Ocean to measure electric fields and other stuff. [7]On the heels of that success, they've proposed a four-year series of experiments at the island. [8]They want to send kites toting 20–30 pounds of meteorological equipment more than ten miles high—about twice the current world record.

[9]The equatorial site's hospitable climate and dependable winds make it an ideal spot for kite experiments, as does the fact that it's not on any major flight routes, which greatly minimizes the risk of entanglements that would be hazardous to planes and fatal to kite researchers' dreams.

47. Which sentence has an error in sentence structure?

   A. Sentence 1
   B. Sentence 3
   C. Sentence 6
   D. Sentence 8

48. Which change should be made?

    A. Sentence 2: Change "hopes" to "hoped"
    B. Sentence 3: Change "they can remain" to "it can remain"
    C. Sentence 5: Change "allows" to "allow"
    D. Sentence 9: Change "make it" to "making it"

49. Which of the following words is an adverb?

    A. usher
    B. hospitable
    C. entanglements
    D. greatly

50. Which sentence contains a level of diction that is inconsistent with the level in the rest of the passage?

    A. Sentence 1
    B. Sentence 5
    C. Sentence 6
    D. Sentence 7

TASP-Based Objective Writing Test, Form B

Name_____

1. _____   20. _____   39. _____

2. _____   21. _____   40. _____

3. _____   22. _____   41. _____

4. _____   23. _____   42. _____

5. _____   24. _____   43. _____

6. _____   25. _____   44. _____

7. _____   26. _____   45. _____

8. _____   27. _____   46. _____

9. _____   28. _____   47. _____

10. _____   29. _____   48. _____

11. _____   30. _____   49. _____

12. _____   31. _____   50. _____

13. _____   32. _____   Score _____

14. _____   33. _____

15. _____   34. _____

16. _____   35. _____

17. _____   36. _____

18. _____   37. _____

19. _____   38. _____

TASP-Based Objective Test Answer Key and Correction Chart, Form B

Question	Answer	Hodges' Section	Writer's Section
1	B	13	31g
2	A	2	18
3	D	3a	19a
4	B	20a	29a
5	B	18c	36c
6	B	18	36
7	A	19d	28d
8	B	3a	19a
9	C	6b	21d
10	C	31b	3c
11	B	32a	1e
12	A	31a	3a
13	D	31c	2d
14	C	2	18
15	C	19c	28c
16	A	7a	22a
17	B	31b	3c
18	D	26a	25a
19	B	27b	N/A
20	A	6b	21d
21	B	32a	1e
22	A	31c	21d
23	D	6b	21d
24	C	4b	20b
25	B	26a	25a
26	B	19c	28c
27	D	2	18
28	C	6a	22e
29	B	31b	3c
30	A	31b	3c
31	D	20a	29a
32	B	3a	19a
33	B	15a	33a
34	D	6a	22e
35	D	20a	29a
36	B	32a	1e
37	B	20a	29a
38	D	32a	1e
39	B	18	13a
40	D	4c	20c
41	A	31c	2d
42	D	6b	21d
43	B	32a	1e
44	B	31b	3c
45	A	32a	1e
46	C	4b	20b
47	B	3a	19a
48	C	6a	22e
49	D	4b	20b
50	C	19c	28c

TASP-Based Essay Test, Form B₁

Essay Directions: Your assignment is to write a multiple-paragraph essay of 300–600 words in response to the following question. You have a minimum of 50 minutes to complete this essay; during that time, you should plan, write, and edit the essay. Do not write a rough draft and recopy.

Grading Criteria

Your essay will be scored holistically on how well it states a whole message to a specific audience for the given purpose. Your essay will be graded on the following criteria:

Appropriateness: Answering the specific question and using appropriate language for the writing situation
Unity and focus: Maintaining your main idea within the essay and within individual paragraphs
Development: Including examples that prove your position
Organization: Sequencing your ideas logically and clearly
Sentence structure: Writing complete and correct sentences
Usage: Using standard grammar and word choices
Mechanics: Using standard capitalization, spelling, and punctuation

Writing Assignment

Should television cameras be allowed in courtrooms? Some people believe that the public has the right to know what occurs during a trial. Others believe that television cameras in the courtroom create a media event, rather than a judicial event.

Your assignment is to write a multiple-paragraph essay, between 300 and 600 words, to be read by a classroom instructor, in which you take a position on this issue. Be sure to defend your position with logical arguments and appropriate examples.

TASP-Based Essay Test, Form B₂

Essay Directions: Your assignment is to write a multiple-paragraph essay of 300–600 words in response to the following question. You have a minimum of 50 minutes to complete this essay; during that time, you should plan, write, and edit the essay. Do not write a rough draft and recopy.

Grading Criteria

Your essay will be scored holistically on how well it states a whole message to a specific audience for the given purpose. Your essay will be graded on the following criteria:

Appropriateness: Answering the specific question and using appropriate language for the writing situation
Unity and focus: Maintaining your main idea within the essay and within individual paragraphs
Development: Including examples that prove your position
Organization: Sequencing your ideas logically and clearly
Sentence structure: Writing complete and correct sentences
Usage: Using standard grammar and word choices
Mechanics: Using standard capitalization, spelling, and punctuation

Writing Assignment

Should the state government have the right to tax purchases made on the Internet? Proponents say that Internet shopping is unfair to local businesses, which have to pay state sales taxes. Opponents say that the Internet sites do not need the services of the state, so why should shoppers have to pay a tax when there is no benefit?

TASP-Based Essay Test, Form B₃

Essay Directions: Your assignment is to write a multiple-paragraph essay of 300–600 words in response to the following question. You have a minimum of 50 minutes to complete this essay; during that time, you should plan, write, and edit the essay. Do not write a rough draft and recopy.

Grading Criteria

Your essay will be scored holistically on how well it states a whole message to a specific audience for the given purpose. Your essay will be graded on the following criteria:

Appropriateness:	Answering the specific question and using appropriate language for the writing situation
Unity and focus:	Maintaining your main idea within the essay and within individual paragraphs
Development:	Including examples that prove your position
Organization:	Sequencing your ideas logically and clearly
Sentence structure:	Writing complete and correct sentences
Usage:	Using standard grammar and word choices
Mechanics:	Using standard capitalization, spelling, and punctuation

Writing Assignment

Should every person in America be tested for AIDS and the results made public? Proponents say that this disease is fatal and that the people have a right to know who is infected and who is not. Opponents say that Americans have the right to privacy and that laws like this one would lead to ostracism of AIDS victims and perhaps killings.

TASP-Based Essay Test, Form B

Answer Sheet

Name_____

Date_____

_____

_____

_____

_____

_____

_____

_____

_____

_____

_____

_____

_____

_____

_____

_____

_____

_____

_____

_____

_____

_____

_____

_____

_____